JOHN

C000133064

Discovering
Watermills

SHIRE PUBLICATIONS LTD

Printed in Great Britain by CIT Printing Services, Press Buildings, Merlins Bridge, Haverfordwest, Dyfed SA61 1XF.

British Library Cataloguing in Publication Data
Vince, John
    Discovering Watermills. - 6Rev. ed. -
(Discovering Books; No. 80)
I. Title II. Series
621. 21   ISBN 0-7478-0206-8

ACKNOWLEDGEMENTS

Since the first edition of this guide appeared many people have written to the author and publishers about watermills. They have now become too numerous to list individually but the author and publishers wish to place on record their appreciation of the contribution these readers and the mill owners have made.

Photographs are acknowledged as follows: A. Booth, page 79; Richard Burn, page 84; Cheshire County Museum Service, page 31; Gay Christiansen, page 63; City of Birmingham, page 90; S. G. Coney, page 47; Crabble Mill, page 62; Durham County Council Planning Department, page 46; The Faversham Society, page 61; Haxted Mill, page 87; Heron Corn Mill, page 5; JB Photography, page 27; F. Leonard Jackson, page 37; Cadbury Lamb, pages 15, 25, 29, 41, 43, 44, 45, 48, 50, 52, 54, 55, 57, 59, 67, 70, 74, 81, 83, 85, 88, 96, 97, 100, 103 and 107; Leeds Industrial Museum, page 93; C. L. Lovell, page 40; The Mill Hotel and Restaurant, page 82; National Trust for Scotland, page 98; Ivor Nicholas, page 35; Quarry Bank Mill Trust, page 30; Anne Ruffell and Paultons Park, page 53; Sheffield Museum, page 78; South Yorkshire County Council, page 77; John Vince, page 66; Martin Watts, pages 39 and 72; Weald and Downland Open Air Museum, page 92; Welwyn Hatfield Museum Service, page 58; Wookey Hole Caves Ltd, page 75.

The cover photograph by K. Westwood is of Daniel's Mill, Eardington, near Bridgnorth, Shropshire. The mill is a fully restored working watermill with a wheel 38 feet in diameter. The photograph is reproduced by kind permission of Mrs J. E. George.

CONTENTS

INTRODUCTION

Archaeologists have uncovered many primitive hand-powered grindstones which were used by early man to grind corn. The first method of pounding grain into a pulp was to use a crude saddle stone. It is very easy for us to overlook the tremendous importance which should be attached to the anonymous genius who contrived the first rotary quernstone. The idea of crushing grain by squeezing it between a revolving stone and a stationary one seems commonplace but this invention was probably the first step on the pathway that led to civilisation. Primeval hunters had to be nomads — or starve; but civilisation demands a different pattern of life based upon a more or less static homestead. A home for all seasons made agriculture possible, and the first people who tended the soil laid the real foundations of society.

It is reasonable to guess that in some parts of the world animal power eventually replaced the woman's hand at the millstone, but little evidence has survived from ancient times to demonstrate this development. At Pompeii huge man-operated mills have been recovered from the devastation wrought by Vesuvius (AD 79). These mills were worked by slaves and their task must have been both tedious and exhausting.

The application of water power to the millstone probably originated in ancient Greece, perhaps in the first century BC. A Roman engineer of this period, Vitruvius, has left us a description of a watermill with a vertical waterwheel and in its essentials it does not differ from those that survive today. The Romans brought it to Britain.

One of the benefits that William the Conqueror has bestowed upon historians is the Domesday Book, which records the extent and value of lands held by his subjects in 1086. Mills were a significant capital asset and they did not escape the eye of his surveyors. Readers who want to find out about Domesday mills do not need to struggle with the original manuscript. The *Victoria County History* has been published for most of the English counties and the local library should have an appropriate copy on its reference shelves. It is an interesting exercise to make a list of Domesday mills and compare it with a list of known mills of more recent date. Although buildings eventually decay, sites have frequently been reused many times.

The main purpose of the watermill was to grind corn but in later ages water power was put to other uses. Waterwheels proved useful to the blacksmith and in the sixteenth century there were many water-powered tilt hammers in the Weald. As maps show, the iron industry left its mark in Surrey and Sussex place-names like Abinger Hammer, Panningridge Furnace, Robertsbridge Forge, Wire Mill, Parrock Forge, Forge Farm and Cansiron.

When the industrial revolution of the eighteenth century got under way it made good use of water power. Streams powered all sorts of factories and, although history books often emphasise the woollen mills, water was also used for copper mills, paper mills, snuff mills, white-lead mills and furniture factories. Water power had a part to play in mining too and the great wheel at Laxey, Isle of Man, is one important monument of this kind. Canals used vast quantities of water and at Claverton, near Bath, the water-powered pumping engine can still be seen.

Watermills have served man for about two thousand years and those that survive today are mostly fashioned on the model described by Vitruvius. A few mills remain in working order and some have been converted into attractive homes. Other mills have vanished – above ground level – but have left their mark on the landscape in the watercourses, dams and sluices men built to serve them. In the pages which follow the principal characteristics of the watermill are described.

No small book can contain all that may be written about watermills and readers who wish to know more should delve into the books listed in 'Further reading' (page 110). The best way to discover watermills is to go out and find them. The author has always found people who live in or work watermills to be very helpful and they often take great trouble and pride in explaining the living history which surrounds them.

Heron Corn Mill and Museum of Papermaking, Beetham, Cumbria.

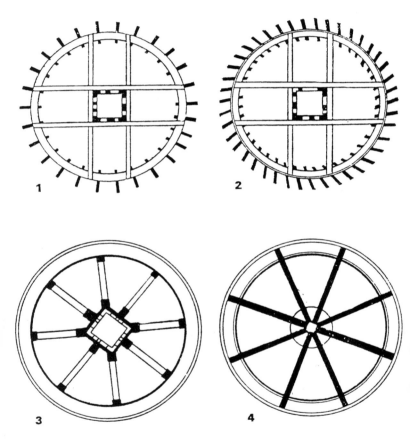

WATERWHEELS. 1. Clasp-arm wooden wheel wedged on to square axletree, with radial paddles. 2. Clasp-arm wheel with open offset paddles. 3. Hybrid wheel with iron rim and centre. 4. Iron wheel and axle with enclosed buckets.

MILL-WHEEL CONSTRUCTION

The first waterwheels were constructed of wood. In the Science Museum at South Kensington, London, there are several interesting models of Saxon waterwheels, but our knowledge of mill machinery from this early period is fragmentary, and even later illuminated manuscripts which illustrate mills or mill wheels supply only a little technical information.

A mill reproduced from a thirteenth-century manuscript in *The Land* by John Higgs (Studio Vista) does show more detail than most early drawings and it is easy to see that the layout of mill machinery did not change significantly in the centuries which followed.

Of the wheels which have survived there are three main types: wooden wheels, metal wheels, and the hybrids made from both.

Wooden wheels

Wooden wheels were mounted on wooden axletrees that were seldom less than 18 inches square in section. These wooden wheels were constructed in the manner indicated on page 6. Two pairs of spokes made up each side of the wheel and as they were set at right angles to each other they clasped the axle in the space created by their intersection — hence they are called clasp-arm wheels. A wheel did not fit exactly around its axle. The final position of the wheel in relation to its hub was determined by the stout wedges that were driven in at each face of the axle. At the ends of the parallel spokes the felloes were fixed and these gave the wheel a recognisable form. Eight segments were common around the rim and each joint was strengthened by the addition of an iron band bolted to each side of the felloe. The stout pegs that supported the paddle boards were mortised through the rim and fixed into place with pins or bolts. Very early wheels of this kind would probably have been held together with wooden pins.

A disused wooden wheel with one half left permanently in the water will gradually decay and its lower members will slowly disappear on the floodwaters of successive winters. An intact wooden wheel is therefore unusual but a few mills may possess a restored one. The watermill enthusiast will normally find that the upper, dry part of the wheel has survived and its condition will depend on the state of the wheelhouse roof. When a mill ceases to work its wheel is frequently jammed with heavy timbers to prevent it from moving if floodwaters spill over the sill. Wheels are seldom left free to move, even if the machinery is out of gear, as they usually set up a considerable amount of vibration if they are allowed to rotate too fast.

Hybrid wheels

The development of cast iron in the eighteenth century allowed many improvements to be made in machines of all kinds. This development will be further discussed below, but the advantages it had to the millwright when it was used in conjunction with timber will be examined here. Clasp-arm wheels were not particularly strong at their centres where their spokes were wedged on to the axletree. A casting, however, could solve the problem and supply a truer and stronger centre. Stronger and more accurate rims could be made in cast iron and this helped to produce a wheel with a better balance. Even working wheels of wood reached a stage when they had to be replaced. The introduction of a new wheel made entirely of metal could be very expensive for the miller, as alterations would have to be made to the internal machinery. The cheapest way of providing a new wheel which had some of the advantages of the metal ones was to construct a wheel on the old — and usually heavy — wooden axle.

This is what happened at the mill known as Tennyson's Mill at Stockworth, near Somersby, Lincolnshire. Here the old axletree was fitted with two cast square bosses, each with eight short radiating arms. Into each of the three-sided boxes a wooden spoke could then be fitted. The inner side of these spoke boxes was open and when the wooden spoke was in place a metal plate was bolted into position to make the fourth side. Two bolts held the plate and the spoke in place and the timber was then firmly housed in the casting. The plate had an important function to perform. As the nuts on the bolts were tightened and the vice-like pressure increased, the metal plate took the strain of compression that would have caused the nuts to become embedded in unprotected timber. Eight spokes arranged at regular intervals made for improved balance but not all the spokes of this wheel are equal in length. Spokes at right angles to the face of the axle are longer than those which spring from the corners (on the diagonal).

At the rim the wooden spokes fit into sockets spaced around its inner edge. In place of the mortised pegs of the wooden wheels, the elm paddles fit neatly into the slots cast on the rim's inner face. There were sound reasons for millers to make use of hybrid wheels and the skill of the millwright enabled him to gain advantages from new and traditional materials at the same time.

Examples of hybrid wheels may be found at Skenfrith, Gwent (a wheel with open paddles and a slender iron rim which is braced with rods); Rossett, Clwyd (also with open paddles); Thrumm Mill, Rothbury, Northumberland (also with open paddles); Tealby, Lincolnshire (a primitive wheel with crude spokes and closed paddles).

Hybrid wheels do not necessarily fit neatly into a theoretical period of time between old wooden wheels and modern cast ones. It seems probable that many, perhaps most, of those that still survive date from a time during the late nineteenth or early twentieth century when a metal wheel could have been used as a replacement. The use of hybrids almost certainly derives from their relative economy.

Cast-iron wheels

Cast iron played an important part in the industrial changes which began in the eighteenth century. One of its advantages was its adaptability. An iron wheel could be made in sections and bolted together in the mill. This fact alone could enable changes to be made more easily and cheaply. A great number of mills must have had old wheels replaced with cast specimens during the eighteenth and nineteenth centuries. Alterations could be made to a mill gradually if cast-iron fittings were to replace wooden ones. In this way major alterations could be spread over a period of time without the miller having to endure long periods when the mill could not be worked.

The outstanding waterwheel in the British Isles is undoubtedly 'The Lady Isabella' at Laxey, Isle of Man. It was constructed in 1854 to pump water from a lead mine and could raise, at two revolutions per minute, 250 gallons of water from a depth of 600 feet. This enormous wheel, which is visited by hundreds of tourists each year, has a diameter of 72 feet 6 inches and is 6 feet in width. During the summer months it is still turned to impress the visitors.

Older wheels can be found, like the iron wheel at Cromford, Derbyshire. This wheel is overshot. It has a cog ring that drives a spur wheel. This is mounted upon the spindle that carries the motion into the mill. The antiquity of this interesting wheel is conveyed by the massiveness of its ironwork.

Other lesser iron wheels preserve the distinction between open or closed paddles. It is always interesting when finding a new wheel to compare the way different millwrights braced the metal paddles to prevent them from becoming distorted by the water. Examples of metal wheels may be found at Billing, Northamptonshire (open paddles); Kersey, Suffolk (open paddles); Molecey House, West Deeping, Lincolnshire (open paddles); Scotsgrove, Buckinghamshire (closed paddles).

WATERWHEELS AT WORK

When the water passes the watergate it has two possible routes on its journey past the wheel: to go over or to go under. Undershot wheels, operated by water passing below the axle, may have been the first to be used as the overshot type usually requires to be more skilfully contrived.

There are two main kinds of undershot wheels: those that are worked by a stream without a sluice, and those that are operated by a head of water built up behind a sluice gate. The former kind has a mechanical efficiency of some 35 per cent. The latter type has two subdivisions: if the water strikes the paddles at about the level of the axle, the wheel is called a high-breast wheel; wheels that are operated by the stream meeting the paddles below the axles are called low-breast wheels. High- and low-breast wheels are 55-60 per cent efficient and this probably accounts for their being more numerous than the plain undershot type. Low-breast wheels are sometimes termed 'four o'clock wheels' for reasons which are explained by the diagram.

Overshot wheels rotate in the opposite direction to the undershot type. They are often to be found in mills in hilly areas, where the narrow streams fall with considerable velocity. In other locations an overshot wheel will require the construction of an embankment to create a sufficient head of water. Overshot wheels are more efficient than the undershot type, with a rating of 68 per cent.

An unusual variation of the overshot wheel is the pitchback wheel. Such wheels rotate in the same direction as undershot ones and the water spills on to the paddles below the apex — or at one o'clock. There was once a mill at Bierton, Buckinghamshire, with a wheel of this type but they seem to be rather rare.

Watercourses

Every watermill has its own individual characteristics that make it unique. The arrangement of the watercourses that power the wheel will depend upon the mill's location. Some mills have bypass sluices that appear to plunge the water into a hole in the ground without any obvious outlet. A few mills have these underground aqueducts that emerge many yards below the mill — usually underneath an overgrown bank that discourages their discovery. Derelict sites can pose considerable problems to the investigator who is seeking to reconstruct the layout. Most mills have an arrangement that is fairly easy to identify even if the building has disappeared. Some typical arrangements are shown on page 12 but the features illustrated may not always be found within sight of the mill, and the investigator must be prepared to spend time working

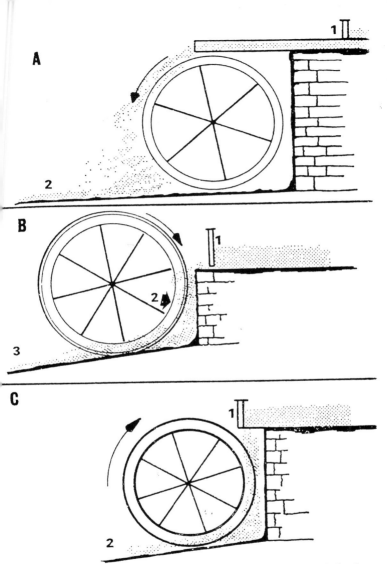

WATERWHEELS. A. Overshot wheel: 1, sluice; 2, tailrace. B. Undershot wheel (high-breast): 1, sluice; 2, alternative position for low-breast wheel; 3, tailrace. C. Pitchback wheel (a variation of the undershot wheel): 1, sluice; 2, tailrace.

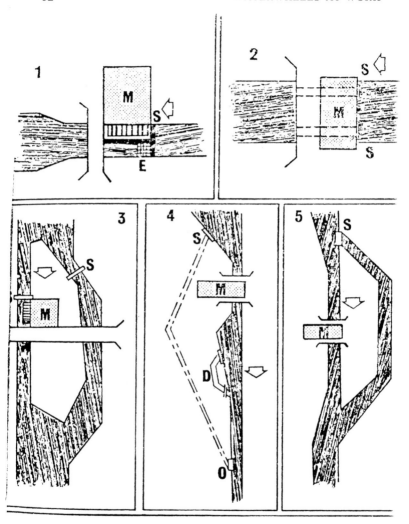

WATERCOURSES. 1. Collateral type: M, mill; S, sluice; E, eel trap. 2. Bridge type (internal wheel): M, mill; S, sluice. 3. Island type: M, mill; S, sluice. 4. Subterranean type: M, mill; S, sluice; O, outfall; D, sheep dip arranged below tailrace. 5. Bypass type: M, mill; S, sluice.

his way through overgrown paths.

Outside the mill it is sometimes possible to find objects connected with the internal machinery. Upstream from one mill the author, in search of the bypass sluice, found a damsel that was being used to operate the mechanism. It made a good lever but it could have been overlooked as it was not in the place one would expect it to be.

The arrangement of the watercourses in relation to the mill is of significance to the historian, and these facts should appear in any notes the investigator may make about the mills he visits. Information about the layout of sluice gates and the disposition of other buildings can be a considerable help if documentary sources are also examined. Mills or mill sites that are about to be redeveloped should be recorded in the fullest detail possible. Events frequently overtake buildings like watermills and if an investigator has a limited time at his disposal he will tend to spend it inside the mill. The actual mill building may be retained while the work of redeveloping the site goes on, and in these circumstances the physical evidence of the watercourses will probably disappear before the mill. It could be that the importance of the mill lies in the way its water supply was arranged. The industrial archaeologist will need to judge the importance of such features and the danger of their complete eradication so that he may apportion his time in the best possible way. A rough sketch plan of a mill with its watergates may be a more useful record for posterity than a measured drawing of a portion of its machinery.

TIDE MILLS

The power of the sea has fascinated man for many centuries and the first successful device he contrived to harness its energy was the tide mill. The principal difference between a tide mill and a conventional watermill lies outside the building. A rising tide brought the water to turn the mill and it was contained in a large millpond. The water was held by watergates, which allowed it to flow only in an upstream direction, and it could escape only through the mill race. The distribution of tide mills was limited to low-lying areas around the coast where large ponds with a relatively low head of water could be created.

One of the disadvantages of a tide mill was the very irregular hours the miller had to work, because the tide reaches its high point at a different time each day. Three or four hours would have to pass after high-water mark before the miller could work the mill as the tide had to recede partly before a head of water was created. A mill could work for less than six hours before the head of water had been consumed and then the miller had to wait for the next tide to replenish his pond. To compensate for a usually low head of water, tide-mill ponds often extended for several acres.

Scattered around the coastline there were a number of tide mills in operation even in the twentieth century; a survivor (Woodbridge, Suffolk) is described in the gazetteer, but most have now vanished. The waterwheels at House Mill and Clock Mill, Bromley-by-Bow, London, remain and the mills, which are scheduled buildings, are owned by the Lea Valley Regional Park Authority. These two mills are probably as far from the sea as any tide mill in the British Isles could be.

It is not known for certain how far back the idea of the tide mill dates — a mill at Dover mentioned in the Domesday Book could have been tidal. More evidence comes from modern times. The Abbey Mill at St Osyth, Essex, demolished in 1963, stood on what is probably the oldest recorded site (c.1413). At East Stonehouse, Devon, the lord of the manor (Sir Peter Edgecumbe) built a causeway in 1526 to create a millpond. Several examples were to be found along the south and east coasts, where the topography lends itself to the establishment of large ponds. George Long lists mills that were working in the early twentieth century: at Eling, Emsworth and Fawley in Hampshire; and at Birdham, Fishbourne and Hermitage in Sussex. Bishopstone Mill, Sussex, had three 15 foot wheels which powered sixteen pairs of stones. The output was reckoned at some 1400 sacks of flour each week. The mill was built in 1761 by the Duke of Newcastle. Thomas Colgate, land agent and surveyor, lived in the mill house in 1911. Other mills

The tide mill at Carew in Dyfed, Wales.

worked at this time were Birdham (William Farne and Sons) and Slipper Mill, Hermitage (Thomas James and Company Ltd). The Isle of Wight had at least three tide mills: East Medina, St Helens and Woolston. Two tide mills were still worked in Pembrokeshire (Dyfed) until just before the Second World War — Carew and Pembroke. In Cornwall tide mills were situated at Antony (Wacker Mill); Antony Passage; Carbeal, Torpoint; Millbrook; and West Looe. Pomphlett Mill, Plymouth, was worked by the tide until 1924. A greater concentration of mills existed along the serpentine shoreline of Essex. There the following mills were worked in 1882, listed with their millers: Fingringhoe (Ezekiel Chopping); St Osyth (Frederick Archer); Stambridge (Alfred and Hugh Rankin); Thorrington (Frederick Cooper) and Walton-on-the-Naze (John Archer).

CORN-GRINDING MACHINERY

The diagram opposite illustrates the layout of the machinery to be found in a typical watermill. In the wheelhouse, if there is one, the wheel generates the motion that is carried into the interior of the mill by the axle (A). At the end of the axle is placed the pit (or pitch) wheel (B). Half of this component is permanently within the narrow pit that gives it its common name. In ancient mills, as at Arlington, Gloucestershire, the pit wheel is usually fashioned of timber. At a later stage of development the wooden wheels were replaced by iron ones. Iron wheels, however, frequently had wooden teeth. This is almost always so when the replacement of a wooden pit wheel did not coincide with the replacement of an original wooden shaft (D). Pit wheels vary in size, and many of the cast variety will be found to bear the ironfounder's name. A close examination of an iron pit wheel will reveal that it is made in two parts that are bolted together. This made the millwright's task much easier. If the axletree was not to be replaced, the pit wheel was divided into two parts for convenience. If a pit wheel was cast whole, it could be installed only if the axle was removed. When one sees how large some pit wheels are, it becomes apparent how sensible the old millwrights were. Even so it could have been no small task to have manoeuvred several hundredweights of cast iron into its required position in a narrow pit so that its complementary half could be bolted to it. A good deal of space was allowed between the axle and the wheel centre so that wedges could be driven in and the wheel correctly centred.

To convert the horizontal line of the axle into a vertical plane the pit wheel meshed into the smaller wallower wheel (C). This latter wheel, frequently of iron, caused the heavy vertical shaft (D) to rotate; and as it had fewer teeth than the pit wheel the speed of the shaft was increased by a ratio of about four or more to one.

Mounted just above the wallower is the spur wheel (E) which carries the motion to the millstones via the stone nut (F). In a mill with a wooden shaft the spur wheel is more often made of wood. A wooden spur wheel will frequently be found to have its spokes morticed into the shaft. Wheels of this kind are called compass-arm wheels as the spokes, usually four, suggest the cardinal compass points. The spur wheel, which rotates at about four times the speed of the axle, is larger and has more teeth than the wallower. When it drives the relatively small stone nut the ratio is again increased by seven or eight to one. A stone nut therefore revolves many times faster than the waterwheel — about 28 to 1. A waterwheel with this sort of gear ratio rotating at nine revolutions per minute will therefore cause the millstone to revolve at approxi-

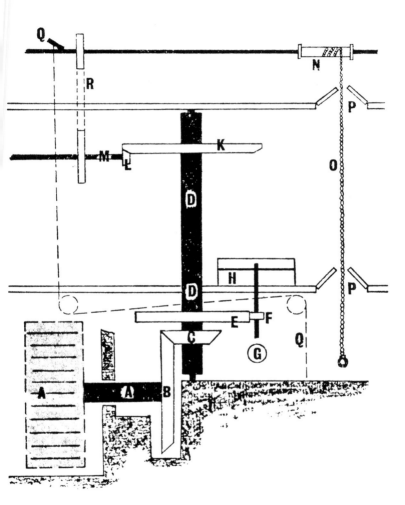

MILL GEARS. A, waterwheel and axletree; B, pit wheel; C, wallower; D, main shaft; E, spur wheel; F, stone nut; G, jack ring (see page 19 for detailed drawing); H, millstones; K, crown wheel; L, bevel gear; M, layshaft; N, sack hoist; O, chain; P, trapdoors; Q, control for sack hoist mechanism; R, belt drive to sack hoist.

mately 270 rpm.

The wooden teeth of the spur wheel mesh with the teeth of the stone nut. Although all the gears in old mills were wooden many mills have had some wooden cog wheels replaced by iron ones. It is a relatively simple task to replace a stone nut as it can be moved without the need to dismantle other minor items of machinery. It is not unusual to find wooden teeth in a mill meshing with iron ones. This was supposed to make for smoother running. Another advantage arose when iron gears were introduced. Technical reasons limited the minimum size of wooden wheels. As iron wheels could be cast with smaller dimensions than those of wooden wheels, iron stone nuts allowed the gear ratio between them and the spur wheel to be increased. This allowed a higher rate of revolution to be produced in the millstone.

If a wooden stone nut was replaced by a smaller iron wheel the vertical axis of the millstones was moved closer to the main shaft. Where this occurred the beams supporting the stones were not always realigned. An observant viewer may sometimes be able to distinguish where this has happened by examining the underside of the bedstone and the relationship of its centre with the surrounding hursting. Care needs to be taken in interpreting the configuration of structural woodwork as it was not unusual for timbers to be reused for different purposes.

Many mills are reputed to contain timbers from a ship and this kind of tradition could easily arise when the heavy beams of an old barn were installed in a mill during a major rebuilding. There is, however, at least one recorded example of this kind. Timber from the 36-gun United States frigate *Chesapeake* (1799) was used in the construction of the Chesapeake Mill at Wickham, Hampshire, after the vessel was broken up in 1819. A model of the ship may be seen in the National Maritime Museum, Greenwich.

The iron stone nut is normally the only adjustable gear wheel in a mill. It can be moved up its square shaft by the jack ring (G), which is operated by the screw mechanism below. A stone nut is lifted out of gear, or lowered into gear, when the mill is not in motion. At the end of the day's work a mill would be left out of gear. This was a sensible precaution for any miller to take. A heavy fall of rain could easily spill over the sluice and start the wheel in his absence. If this happened, a mill left in gear could run hot, ruin the stones or even catch fire.

On the stone floor the crown wheel (K) provides the drive to the bevel gear (L), which turns the layshaft (M), on which are mounted various pulleys. During a mill's working life machines like oat crushers were driven from the layshaft. One of the most important devices operated from the layshaft was the sack hoist (N), which played such an important part in a miller's day. The sack hoist was able to work only when the wheel was in motion. From the bin floor the long chain (O) passed down through the trapdoors (P) to the ground. Trapdoors opened upwards as the diagram (page 17) shows. This was an excellent arrangement. The sack was hoisted upwards and the doors automatically dropped back into position after it had passed through. As we shall see below, this was the usual direction full sacks took through the mill.

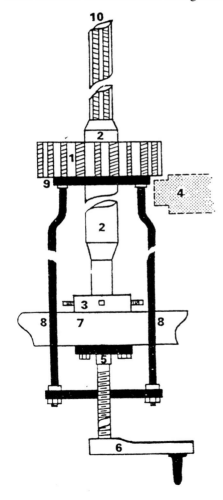

JACK RING.
The ring is shown in out of gear position.
1, stone nut; 2, square section of shaft; 3, bearing with screw adjustment for alignment; 4, spur wheel; 5, pressure plate; 6, handle; 7, beam of hurst frame; 8, arms; 9, jack ring; 10, splined end of shaft to drive runner stone.
See also diagram on page 17.

GRINDING THE GRAIN

The path taken by the grain through the millstones is shown in the diagram opposite. Millers knew the effects of gravity long before it was 'discovered' by Isaac Newton. Corn was first taken, via the sack hoist, to the top of the mill, where it was placed in the grain bin. A chute led to the hopper positioned above the millstones. Grain trickled from the bottom of the hopper on to the feed shoe, which was methodically shaken by the damsel. As the upper runnerstone revolved, so a few grains were fed into the eye to the ground and expelled around the stones' circumference — guided by the grooves on the face of the millstone. The meal then fell into the meal spout and finally into the bin on the floor below. The effect of the grinding process was to make the emerging meal quite warm, and anyone feeling it for the first time usually expresses surprise at its temperature.

In their heyday most mills operated two types of stone: barley was worked on Derbyshire Peak stones; flour was prepared on French burr stones, which were more suitable for finer grinding. These latter stones were not made in one piece, like the Derbyshire Peaks, but in sections cemented together. The outer edge of the stone was bound with iron bands, usually two.

Only the upper (runner) stone revolved and it did not come into contact with the bedstone below as many people think. The space between the surfaces of the stones was minute and carefully controlled to produce the best results. Millstones, like waterwheels, often needed to have a small weight added to them in order to get them to run true — without any irregular vibrations. Motorists may be familiar with the effect an unbalanced wheel can have on a car! A millstone, weighing anything up to a ton, could produce its own dramatic aberrations if it was not in balance.

Stones driven by a common spur wheel revolve in the same direction. The mode of revolution determined the pattern on the grinding faces. It is an interesting exercise to work out the manner in which stones rotate. A mill with an undershot wheel and another with an overshot wheel will have stones moving in opposite directions. Where mills ground only grist one pair of stones was usually sufficient to cope with the miller's trade.

From the revolutions given on page 22 it is possible to calculate the number of revolutions per minute made by a given waterwheel. The ratio of the gears needs to be known and in order to assist counting investigators are recommended to carry a piece of chalk to mark the point at which their addition begins. It is very easy to become distracted and lose count but if cogs are marked off in tens the operation is usually more accurate!

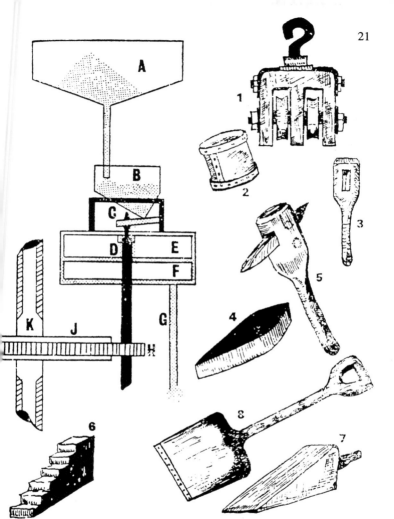

21

GRINDING THE GRAIN. A, hopper on bin floor; B, hopper; C, feed shoe; D, damsel to shake feed shoe; E, runnerstone; F, bedstone; G, chute to meal bin; H, stone nut; J, spur wheel; K, main shaft.

ARTEFACTS. 1, pulley block used to lift stones for dressing; 2, peck measure; 3, thrift; 4, mill bill; 5, mill bill fixed in thrift; 6, 'many heights', a form of wedge use to jack up millstones; 7, wedge with handle; 8, meal shovel, carved from a single piece of sycamore.

Work done by millstones

Stone diameters (inches)	30	36	42	48
Quantity of corn ground into fine flour per hour (bushels)	$2^1/_2$	$3^1/_4$	4	5
Produce of meal from ditto, at 60 pounds to the bushel (pounds)	150	190	240	300
Produce of fine dressed flour from ditto, for making bread (pounds)	90	120	150	180
Quantity of corn ground into coarse meal for cattle feed (bushels)	5	$6^1/_2$	8	10
Produce of meal from ditto for cattle feed (pounds)	300	390	490	610
Number of revolutions of stones per minute	250	200	185	150
Horsepower required	2	3	4	5

Speeds in corn mills (rpm)

Revs per minute

Stones 4 feet in diameter	150
Dressing machines 21 inches in diameter	450-500
Elevators, pulleys, 18 inches in diameter	40
Wheat screen 18 inches in diameter	300-350

WATERMILLS IN ENGLAND

Since the first edition of this book appeared many mills have been restored and opened to the public. Much of the labour of restoration has been carried out by voluntary enterprise.

Every year thousands of visitors support the work of conservation and renewal by their entry fees. Enlightened public bodies have also financed the reinstatement of many important industrial monuments. Local government has often co-operated with voluntary organisations so that projects which would have been financially impossible have been brought to fruition.

Mills require constant care and repair, and from time to time temporary closures are essential. Ownership may also change, and this usually causes visiting arrangements to be altered.

The mills listed below are mostly open to the public, though some only on a very restricted basis. The arrangements indicated were correct at the time of going to press but readers are advised to check details of opening times before setting out. A number of mill sites recorded are open only under the National Gardens Scheme and readers should consult the annual guide *Gardens of England and Wales Open to the Public* to check the exact days of opening — usually one or two — in any given year. Where appropriate, indications concerning arrangements for organised parties are also noted. Many of the mills listed below make excellent venues for adult classes or school parties and some provide special educational facilities.

The author and publishers will be pleased to receive corrections and notes on other mills for inclusion in subsequent editions.

AVON

Blaise Castle House Museum, Henbury, Bristol.

Stratford Mill, which formerly stood at West Harptree, Avon, has been re-erected here. This mill was at work until 1952. Although the mill is now closed it can be viewed by appointment with the curator. The museum collections illustrate English domestic, urban and rural life. Museum open: Saturday to Wednesday, 10-1, 2-5; closed Thursday and Friday. Please telephone to confirm opening times before making a visit. Contact: David Eveleigh, Curator, Blaise Castle House Museum, Henbury, Bristol BS10 7QS (telephone: 0272 506789).

Claverton Pumphouse, Ferry Lane, Claverton.

This superb engine was built to John Rennie's design in 1813 to lift water from the river Avon to the Kennet and Avon Canal, 48 feet above on the hillside. The waterwheel is in two sections mounted upon a single axle. The width is 24 feet, the diameter 17 feet 6 inches, and the total weight about 20 tons. The capacity of the paddles is 3 to 4 tons of water at each contact. As this vast breastshot wheel turns it operates a cast-iron pit wheel 16 feet in diameter, with 204 wooden teeth. These teeth mesh with a follower wheel 5 feet 3 inches in diameter, with 64 teeth. A flywheel and crankshaft on the follower's axle generate the motion for the connecting rods that are attached to the two heavy beams. These move the piston rods up and down in each of the two cylinders of the pump. At first sight the pump looks like a beam engine. After a mishap with a floating log in 1952 the pump ceased working and by 1969 was in a state of dereliction. In 1975, after more than ten thousand hours of labour by members of the Kennet and Avon Trust, the pump was restored to its present working state. It is one of England's most impressive water-powered engines. Open: April to October, Sundays, 10.30-1 and 2-5. On Bank Holiday Sundays and Mondays (Christmas excepted) it may be seen at work. Information and party bookings: Brian Perrington, 9 Lincoln Close, Keynsham, Bristol, Avon BS18 2LJ (telephone: 0272 867536).

Priston Mill, near Bath.
6 miles south-west of Bath between A39 and A367.
   This is a working mill with an unusual pitchback wheel. There has been a mill on this site since the tenth century. In the eighteenth century the mill also possessed a tucking stock for felting cloth. Open daily from Easter to the end of September, Monday to Saturday 2.15-5, Sundays and Bank Holidays 11-5.30. Parties are welcome by appointment at any time of the year. Guided tours and evening visits can be arranged. The mill shop sells stoneground flour and refreshments. Contact: Priston Mill, Priston, near Bath, Avon BA2 9EQ (telephone: 0225 423894 or 429894; fax: 0225 421601).

BEDFORDSHIRE

Bromham Mill, Bromham.
Next to the ancient bridge on the north side of A428.
   This mill has a particularly fine setting. There was probably a mill here in 1086. The structure has been rebuilt following a fire in 1974. Parts of it date from the late seventeenth and early eighteenth centuries. There is a 14 foot by 7 foot wide breast wheel which replaced an earlier one in 1908. It was made by Austee of Kempston and works two pairs of Peak stones. Milling takes place at regular intervals. In the 1920s a steam engine provided power when the water level in the Ouse was low. Grinding ceased in 1943. A well-

Bromham Mill, Bedfordshire.

illustrated guidebook is available. Party visits at any time by arrangement. Picnic area. Open: April to October, Wednesday to Friday 10.30-4.30, Saturday, Sunday and Bank Holidays 11.30-6. Contact: Sally Wileman, Leisure Services Department, Bedfordshire County Council, County Hall, Bedford MK42 9AP (telephone: 0234 228330).

BERKSHIRE

The Mill, Sonning.

The Domesday Book (1086) mentioned three mills at Sonning. When Reading was a garrison town for Cromwell's troops during the Civil War Sonning Mill provided their flour. The present mill building dates, in part, from the eighteenth century. Until 1950 the mill had its own fleet of barges which brought grain up from London. Sonning Mill provided flour for Huntley & Palmers' biscuits until it ceased to work in 1969. The building remained unused until the present owners converted it into a theatre in 1982. Two wheels remain. The larger one, which was the most powerful wheel on the Thames, is now anchored. In its working days it sometimes 'ran away'. It can still be seen behind its glass screen. The smaller wheel still turns and is a feature of the bar area. No other machinery remains. Open only to patrons. Telephone: 0734 698000.

Watermill Theatre, Bagnor, Newbury.

On a Domesday site, the 1830s mill was converted to a theatre in

1967. The original wheel is still in position and can be viewed. Open: March to January (theatre and restaurant). Contact: Jill Fraser, Watermill Theatre, Bagnor, Newbury, Berkshire RG16 8AE (telephone: 0635 45834).

BUCKINGHAMSHIRE

Ford End Mill, Ivinghoe.
On the west side of the B488 Linslade Road.
   The mill has three storeys set beneath a distinctive mansard roof that is unusual in this part of England. An iron overshot wheel, 11 feet in diameter by 5 feet wide, drives two pairs of stones and ancillary equipment. This mill has been painstakingly restored to working order by the Pitstone Local History Society. The area below the tailrace was formerly used as a sheepwash. Milling demonstrations take place on National Mills Day, Bank Holidays in May and August, and on the second Sunday afternoon in June, July and September. Other demonstrations by arrangement. Open: May to September, Sundays 2.30-5.30. Party visits arranged (telephone: 0296 668826). Other enquiries to Mr David Lindsey, Watermill Secretary (telephone: 0582 600391).

Hambleden Mill
   This is one of the most picturesque mills on the Thames. Its white-boarded sides make it a prominent feature. There is a footbridge which allows the visitor to cross the weirs.

Pann Mill, The Rye, High Wycombe.
   This mill ceased work in 1967, when it was demolished. The interesting waterwheel was left *in situ* for several years as a landscape feature. The machinery has now been reassembled in a reconstructed building created in 1984 by the High Wycombe Society with the financial support of Marks & Spencer plc. The exhibition includes artefacts related to milling. Visitors are welcome to view the only corn mill remaining on the river Wye. There is a public car park in Easton Street opposite the mill. Open as advertised during the year or by arrangement. Contact: Mrs Myra King (telephone: 0494 523698).

CAMBRIDGESHIRE

Houghton Mill, near Huntingdon.
On the river Ouse about 2 miles downstream from Huntingdon.
   This mill is a National Trust property. There has been a mill on this island site since 1086. At one time there were three large

Working on the wheel at Pann Mill, High Wycombe, Buckinghamshire.

undershot wheels. Corn is ground every Sunday when the mill is open. Open: April to October, Saturday, Sunday and Bank Holiday Monday 2-5.30; in school summer holidays open also on Monday, Tuesday and Wednesday. Parties at other times by arrangement. Contact: Alan Forrest, Custodian, Houghton Mill, Houghton, St Ives, Cambridgeshire (telephone: 0480 301494).

Lode Mill, Anglesey Abbey, Lode.

Acquired in 1966 by the National Trust with the Anglesey Abbey Estate, the mill was constructed in the eighteenth century and last worked in 1910. Restoration has been carried out by the Cambridgeshire Wind and Watermill Society and most of the machinery is now intact and restored. Unusually, the mill is weatherboarded vertically rather than horizontally. Open: April to October, Wednesday and Friday 1.30-5.15. Corn is ground on the first Sunday of each month. Contact: Graham Moran, Administrator, Anglesey Abbey, Lode, Cambridgeshire CB5 9EJ (telephone: 0223 811200).

Maxey Mill
On the river Welland, one mile from Market Deeping.

This is a fully operating mill producing pig food to support a pig herd. It is the third mill on this site and the present three-storey building dates from 1779. It has a clasped-arm breastshot wheel, 13 feet 4 inches in diameter, driving two pairs of stones. The mill is working most afternoons but before travelling visitors should telephone Mr and Mrs D. Stables on 0778 343191.

Sacrewell Mill, Thornhaugh (William Scott Abbott Trust).
Half a mile north-east of the A1/A47 junction. Access is on the north side of A47 about a quarter of a mile from the A1 intersection. Look for the tourist signs 'Sacrewell Farm Centre'.

The extant mill house and buildings, restored in 1992 to English Heritage standards by the architect Kenneth Major, date from *c.*1755-60. The 18 foot by 5 foot wide pitchback wheel was probably installed *c.*1820. The site was used for milling at the time of the Domesday survey. There are two pairs of working stones, Derbyshire and French burr, which are used for demonstration purposes. The mill is the focus of the Sacrewell Farm and Country Centre, which includes a display on the farm's history, farm animals, a large collection of farming and domestic bygones, a visitor centre and a shop. Guidebook and refreshments available. Group and school visits by arrangement; teachers' leaflet. Visitor centre open daily 9-5.30. Mill open from 9 and during daylight hours. Contact: David Powell, Sacrewell, Thornhaugh, Peterborough PE8 6HJ (telephone: 0780 782222).

CHESHIRE

Bunbury Watermill, Bunbury.
3 miles south of Tarporley, in Mill Lane, off Bowes Gate Lane, Bunbury, between A49 and A51.

The mill was built *c.*1850. It was worked until 1960, when the millpond was breached during a storm and the water supply was lost. In 1977 the mill was reinstated to its present working order. Some 260 new wooden cogs were made to replace the old teeth, and the wheel was provided with new elm buckets. The process of flourmaking, from grain cleaning to stone grinding, is demonstrated by the Warden, and samples of stoneground flour are available. Open: Easter to September, Saturday, Sunday and Bank Holidays 2-5. Contact: the Warden, Mr D. Buchanan, 14 Clare Drive, Wistaston, Crewe, Cheshire CW2 8ED (telephone: 0270 665667). Group bookings by arrangement with the Warden.

Nether Alderley Mill
2 miles south of Alderley Edge on east side of A34.

A National Trust property, this stone-roofed mill, which has its origins in the fifteenth century, was worked until 1939. The machinery has been restored to working order and flour is ground for

Bunbury Mill, Cheshire, is administered by North West Water.

demonstration purposes. There are two overshot wheels. Open: April, May and October, Wednesday, Sunday and Bank Holidays 1-4.30; June to September, Tuesday to Sunday and Bank Holiday Mondays 1-5. Party visits arranged by Mrs P. Ferguson, 7 Oak Cottages, Styal, Wilmslow, Cheshire (telephone: 0625 523012). Contact: Barbara Morley, National Trust, Attingham Park, Shrewsbury, Shropshire SY4 4TP (telephone: 074377 343).

Quarry Bank Mill, Styal Country Park.

This mill on the river Bollin was built by Samuel Greg in 1784. Quarry Bank is an original water-powered cotton mill. Here you can see how the industrial revolution looked when it began, and how humanitarian concepts were applied to the new factory system. As well as the mill, the visitor should see the village with its chapel, school, cottages and apprentice house. The immense waterwheel, 22 feet wide by 24 feet in diameter, is of special technical interest. It was installed in its restored state in 1986. This is the only surviving suspension wheel built by William Fairbairn and can generate 100 horsepower. The tailrace from the wheel is carried by a tunnel and discharges three-quarters of a mile downstream. From this vast wheel a vertical shaft transfers the power to the weaving shed. A new gallery within the museum explains the development of water power during the industrial revolution. Quarry Bank Mill is owned by the National Trust and leased to the Quarry Bank Mill Trust. Open: October to May, daily except Mondays 11-4 (April and May, 11-5); June to September, daily 11-5; open Bank Holiday Mondays. For Christmas holiday openings,

Fred Madders, former Director of Engineering Services at Quarry Bank Mill, Styal, stands beside the restored Fairbairn iron waterwheel.

Stretton Mill stands in a picturesque setting south of Wrexham. It is an award-winning working museum administered by Cheshire County Museum Service.

further information and party bookings contact: Quarry Bank Mill Trust Ltd, Styal, Cheshire SK9 4LA (telephone: 0625 527468).

Stretton Mill
South of A534 to Wrexham, 3 miles west of junction with A41.

A mill operated here from the fourteenth century until 1959. It was taken over by Cheshire County Council in the 1970s and restored as a working museum, opening in 1978. There are two wheels, one overshot, the other breastshot and with a sluice mechanism which permits the entry of water at three different levels. Open: April to September, Tuesday to Sunday 1-5; March and October, weekends only. There are a picnic area and a viewing area alongside the millpond and there is a shop. Group visits by arrangement from March to October. Contact: Stephen Penny, Cheshire Museums, 162 London Road, Northwich, Cheshire CW9 8AB (telephone: 0606 41331).

CLEVELAND

Tocketts Mill, Guisborough.
One mile east of Guisborough on the A173 Skelton road.

The present four-storey building, with two-storey house attached, dates mainly from the mid nineteenth century. It operated until 1960 and when work finished much of the machinery was left intact. Restoration by staff and students of South Park Sixth Form

College, Middlesbrough, began in 1976 and the mill is now in working order. It is operated by the Cleveland Buildings Preservation Trust Ltd. There is an 18 foot diameter pitchback wheel restored by John Hauxwell & Son of Yarm, the original millwrights. Flour is ground most Sundays. There are related displays of patterns and implements. Open: mid May to September, Sundays 2-4; last entrance 3.30; also on Easter Sunday and National Mills Day. Contact for party visits and admissions: Peter Morgan, 22 Wheatlands, Great Ayton, Middlesbrough, Cleveland TS9 6ED (telephone: 0642 722897).

CORNWALL

Cutcrew Sawmills, Tideford, near Saltash.
Off A38 to St Germans, half a mile past Heskyn Mill.

One of four mills on the river Tiddy, this was built in the late eighteenth century as a corn mill but was shortly converted to an estate sawmill. It was in use under water power until 1958 and was unoccupied for twenty years. The wheel and most internal workings remain and are being restored. The mill now houses wood craftsmen. There are a shop and tearoom. Open: daily 9-6. Telephone: 075538 402.

Dairyland Farm World, Summercourt, Newquay.
4 miles from Newquay on A3058.

The exhibition at this extensive country life museum includes three working waterwheels: one is 36 inches by 9 inches, was made by Irons Bros of Wadebridge and operates twin water pumps; another is a 64 by 12 inch mining wheel made by Bartle & Son of Redruth *c.*1850; the third is a 44 by 12 inch wheel built by G. H. Harris of Wadebridge *c.*1900. Picnic garden. Curriculum notes for teachers. Open: Easter week and May to September, daily 10.30-5.30; April and October, daily 12-5. Coaches and parties by arrangement. Contact: Rex Davey, Tresillian Barton, Summercourt, Newquay, Cornwall TR9 5AA (telephone: 0872 510246).

Lanreath Mill and Farm Museum, Churchtown, Lanreath.

This farm museum contains the reassembled gears and stones from a mill at Treguddick Manor, Launceston. There is no waterwheel. Open: Easter to June and October, daily except Saturdays 11-5; July to September, daily except Saturdays 10-6. Contact: L. Facey, Lanreath Folk and Farm Museum, Lanreath, Looe, Cornwall (telephone: 0503 220321).

Morden Mill, Cotehele.
On the west bank of the Tamar, 8 miles south-west of Tavistock.

The mill is owned by the National Trust and forms part of the Cotehele estate, which includes one of the least altered medieval houses in Britain. Parts of the present mill date from the eighteenth century. The water supply comes from the Morden stream and reaches the wheel via a launder. The mill machinery has been restored to working order. There are also a cider house, blacksmith's forge, wheelwright's shop and carpenter's shop on the mill site. Open: April to September, daily 11-5.30; October, daily 11-5. Use the car park at Cotehele Quay. Contact: the Administrator, Cotehele House (National Trust), St Dominick, Saltash, Cornwall PL12 6TA (telephone: 0579 50434).

Wheal Martyn Museum, Carthew.

There are two working wheels to be seen in this china-clay museum. Both have cranked axles which, through a system of driving rods, work pumps some distance from the wheels. The 35 foot pitchback wheel worked plunger pumps 1000 yards away; the 18 foot overshot wheel still operates a pump that moves 25 gallons of clay slurry at each stroke. Gift and coffee shop; picnic area. Parties by arrangement. Open: Easter to October, daily 10-6. Contact: Wheal Martyn Museum, Carthew, St Austell, Cornwall PL26 8XG (telephone: 0726 850362).

CUMBRIA

Eskdale Corn Mill, Boot.

About a quarter of a mile from Dalegarth station (Ravenglass & Eskdale Railway), on the road to Hardknott Pass.

Pedestrian access to this historic corn mill is via a seventeenth-century packhorse bridge over Whillan Beck at the northern end of Boot village. There are two waterwheels and early wooden machinery. There is a picnic area with waterfalls and woodland. An exhibition illustrates the history and technique of milling oats, barley and wheat. Open: Easter to September, Tuesday to Saturday and Bank Holidays 11-5. Visitors are requested not to park in Boot village; car parking and refreshments are available at Dalegarth station. Information and party bookings: the Custodian (telephone: 09467 23335).

Gleaston Watermill

North of the village of Gleaston; signposted from A5087.

The three-storey stone mill dates from 1774. The high-breast wheel is 18 feet in diameter and works the eighteenth-century machinery, which includes an 11 foot diameter clasp-arm pit wheel. There are four pairs of millstones and a drying kiln. Milling and farming artefacts are on display. This mill was operated until the 1940s and restoration work began in 1989. Disabled visitors are welcome: there is wheelchair access to most of the site. School, other party visits and coaches by arrangement. Guided tours of the mill with demonstrations. Shop; licensed restaurant and café. Open: Easter to September, daily except Monday 11-5; October to Easter daily except Monday 11-4. Open on Bank Holiday Mondays. Contact: Mrs V. Brerton, Gleaston Mill, Gleaston, Ulverston, Cumbria LA12 0QH (telephone: 0229 869244).

Heron Corn Mill and Museum of Papermaking, Beetham.

Off A6 south of Milnthorpe. Tourist signs direct the visitor to the mill.

The name is derived from the heronry which formerly existed just to the north of the mill's picturesque position. Dating from *c.*1735, the mill remained in use until 1955. After restoration, the mill is in working order and milling demonstrations are a regular part of the programme. Cereal products are on sale. Teachers' notes and pupil materials are available. The 14 foot breastshot wheel worked four pairs of stones using the power derived from the river Bela. In 1988 a museum of papermaking was established to mark five centuries of papermaking in Britain. Open: 1st April or Easter (whichever is earlier) to September, Tuesday to Sunday and Bank Holiday Mondays 11-5. Parties also admitted in March and October by arrangement. Contact: the Administrator, c/o Henry Cooke Makin, Waterhouse Mills, Beetham, Milnthorpe, Cumbria LA7 7AR (telephone: 05395 63363; fax: 05395 63869).

Muncaster Mill, Ravenglass.

The entrance lies beside A595 where it crosses the Ravenglass & Eskdale Railway. Trains stop by request.

Although the present building dates from the eighteenth century there has been a mill on this site since at least 1455. The mill stopped work in 1961. It was renovated in 1976-7 and has milled flour since 1978. This is a two-storey oatmeal mill typical of upland Britain. The water comes from the river Mite via a leat about ¾ mile long. The 13 foot overshot wheel is protected by a lean-to wheelhouse open at one end. The stones, driven by a layshaft, are in daily use. There are French burrs, Peak stones and shelling stones. The ancillary machinery includes a flour dresser of 1850, oatmeal shaker, wire machine, winnower and elevators. The kiln attached to the mill has also been restored. Open daily except Saturday: April, May and September 11-5; June to August 10-6. Party visits at other times by appointment. Parking is limited close to the mill but there is a good parking space a short distance away. Information and bookings: Muncaster Mill, Ravenglass, Cumbria CA18 1ST (telephone: 0229 717232).

Muncaster Mill, Ravenglass, Cumbria, has three pairs of millstones on the first floor.

Priests Mill, Caldbeck.

This early eighteenth-century working mill has an undershot wheel. The Lakeland stone buildings were restored in 1985 and there is now an attractive café overlooking the river. This site includes several shops and workshops and the Watermill Museum. Open: mid March to October, Tuesday to Sunday and Bank Holidays 10.30-5; November and December, Saturday and Sunday only. Group visits by arrangement. Contact: Priests Mill, Caldbeck, Cumbria CA7 8DR (telephone: 06998 369).

The Watermill, Little Salkeld, Penrith.

In the Eden valley about one mile north of Langwathby (A686).

This mill has two 12 foot overshot wheels. One wheel is 4 feet 9 inches wide, develops about 15 horsepower and drives two pairs of stones. Nicholas and Ana Jones run a working mill producing about 200 tons of flour each year from organically grown wheat. At the mill shop visitors can purchase flour, porridge oats and oatmeal. Educational visits are a speciality. Open: Mondays to Fridays 10.30-5. Mill tours: Monday, Tuesday and Thursday 11-12 and 2.30-3.30. Contact: Ana Jones, The Watermill, Little Salkeld, Penrith, Cumbria CA10 1NN (telephone: 076881 523).

Wythop Mill, Embleton.

Off A66 4 miles from Cockermouth.

This corn mill was converted to a sawmill in 1860. The present overshot waterwheel was installed at that time. It now drives an exhibition of vintage woodworking machinery. There are displays of hand tools. Coffee shop and licensed restaurant. Open: April to October, daily (but closed Mondays except Bank Holidays) 10.30-5.30; November, December, February and March, Friday, Saturday and Sunday 10.30-4. Group visits by arrangement. No coaches. Contact: J. Sealby, Wythop Mill, Embleton, Cockermouth, Cumbria CA13 9YP (telephone: 07687 76394).

DERBYSHIRE

Alport Mill, Alport.

Just off B5056.

This mill on the river Lathkill is now used as a store, but it has a fine 21 foot diameter by 5 foot wide rim-drive wheel.

Bakewell

North of the crossroads in the town centre, on the right of A6.

This nineteenth-century mill now serves as a laboratory. It has a large iron rim-drive breastshot wheel, 16 feet in diameter by 13 feet wide.

Caudwell's Mill, Rowsley.
On the south edge of the village. Turn off A6 near the Peacock Hotel.

This water-powered roller mill on the river Wye was built in 1874. The traditional waterwheels were replaced in 1887 by a water turbine. The mill produces fine-quality bread flour and is open to visitors in parties of twelve or more by prior arrangement. Special open days, which usually coincide with public holidays, are advertised. Wholemeal flour is always on sale. Enquiries to the Mill Manager (telephone: 0629 734374).

Chatsworth Park Mill, Chatsworth.
The remains of the mill can be seen at the south end of Chatsworth Park opposite the large car park on B6012.

The eighteenth-century estate mill with its low-breast iron and wood wheel was badly damaged in a storm in 1962. The weir across the river Derwent and the mill leat (also called a goit in this part of England) can still be seen. A large Peak stone stands outside the mill.

Cromford

There is a rim-drive wheel in Water Lane outside David Tye's garage. This wheel was used to operate paint-manufacturing ma-

At Cromford, Derbyshire, this iron wheel has a rim drive. The power from the wheel was transferred to a smaller spur wheel that engaged the teeth on the waterwheel's rim.

chinery. Higher up Water Lane, on the left-hand side, the Arkwright
Centre is hidden by another garage. This corn mill is thought to
have been built by Richard Arkwright c.1780. No machinery
remains but the Arkwright Society intends to re-establish this as a
working mill and museum.

Ible Mill
On A5012 half a mile south of Grangemill.
On the east side of the road there is a small ruined mill. Frag-
ments of the machinery remain.

Osmaston Mill
The overshot wheel of the old sawmill can still be seen from the
bridlepath (at map reference SK 208429).

DEVON

Bickleigh Mill and Craft Centre and Farms
This mill was a corn mill until the 1950s when the weir broke,
the wheels stopped and the machinery was removed. In 1972 the
wheel and ancient machinery were restored and a craft centre was
established, with farm shop, agricultural museum and picnic centre. Open Easter to December, daily, except Christmas Day and
Boxing Day, 10-6 (November and December 10-5); January to
Easter, Saturdays and Sundays 10-5. Information and bookings:
Bickleigh Mill, Bickleigh, near Tiverton, Devon EX16 8RG (telephone: 08845 419).

Coldharbour Mill (The Working Wool Museum), Uffculme, Cullompton.
The waterwheel, installed in 1897, is breastshot, 18 feet in
diameter and 14 feet wide between the rims. The cast-iron rims are
connected to the hub by eight main tension rods. There is a
sophisticated hatch system supplying water to the 48 buckets on
the wheel's circumference. The wheel is in process of restoration
and not yet fully operational. In 1865 the mill bought a beam
engine. The Coldharbour Mill Trust has been given a Kittoe &
Brotherhood Beam Engine (c.1867) to replace those scrapped
early in the twentieth century, and in 1910 a Pollit & Wigzel steam
engine was installed, which, together with the wheel, drove the
mill until 1978. The engine is in steam and working on special
weekends as advertised: telephone for details. Coldharbour Mill's
Power Trail for schoolchildren illustrates the history of power.
Open: Easter to October, daily 11-5; telephone for details of winter
opening. Group bookings by appointment, including evenings.
Contact: Miss J. E. Taylor, Coldharbour Mill, Uffculme, near

Crowdy Mill in Devon has two contra-rotating waterwheels.

Cullompton, Devon EX15 3EE (telephone: 0884 840960).

Crowdy Mill, Harbertonford.

A rural corn mill on a site that dates back to the thirteenth century, the present building is probably late Georgian and has an additional floor of 1900. Two contra-rotating wheels, an unusual feature, are powered by the Harbourne river. There are three pairs of stones, a hoist and cleaning and flour-dressing machines. After about thirty years of disuse the mill was put back to work in 1984. Stoneground flour is on sale most weekday afternoons and at other times by appointment with the miller, Keith Benton. A small shop sells farm products. Open daily 10-5. Group bookings by appointment. Contact: Mrs Ann Benton, Crowdy Mill, Harbertonford, Totnes, Devon TQ9 7HU (telephone: 0803732 340).

Hele Mill, Hele Bay, Ilfracombe.

Four minutes walk from Hele Beach and one mile east of Ilfracombe.

Hele Mill contains one of the earliest porcelain roller mills and much other machinery driven by a complex system of flat belts. These are powered either by the 18 foot diameter waterwheel or by the 1927 diesel engine that is used as a stand-by in times of low water. The machinery has clear notices which explain the function of each part. The structure of the mill dates from *c.*1525. The wooden wheel and the old cogpit were modernised in 1927. At that

Hele Mill, Devon, has been restored to working order and produces stoneground flour all through the year.

time the roof was raised to provide extra storage space. After 1945 the mill became derelict. Eventually trees grew through the roof and the wooden buckets of the wheel rotted away. In 1974 restoration work began and the mill has worked continuously since 1978. Stoneground flour is produced all the year round. There is always someone in attendance who can answer questions. Open: Easter to October, Monday to Friday 10-5, Sunday 2-5; closed Saturdays. Contact: C. Lovell, Hele Mill, Ilfracombe, Devon EX32 9QY (telephone: 0271 863185).

Morwellham Quay, Tamar Valley, near Tavistock.

Morwellham was once the greatest copper port in the Victorian empire. After years of neglect the site has been brought back to life by the Morwellham Recreation Company Ltd, a charitable company established by the Dartington Amenity Research Trust. There are three waterwheels. A 34 foot overshot wheel (*c.*1908), which came from the clay workings at Headon Down, Dartmoor, is located on the site of the former manganese mill. The second wheel was used to pump water for the village supply. At Morwellham Farm there is a water-powered threshing box that is worked for demonstration purposes (except at off-peak times). Water power is also to be seen in action at the hydro-electric power station. There are many other attractions for visitors. Open daily (except Christmas Day) 10-6, but from November to March closes at dusk. Information and party bookings: Morwellham Quay, Tavistock, Devon (telephone: 0822 832766).

Museum of Water Power (The Finch Foundry Trust), Sticklepath, Okehampton.

In the centre of Sticklepath village, a mile off A30.

The Finch Foundry is a small water-powered edge-tool factory which made sickles, scythes, shovels, etc, from 1814 to 1960. Five generations of the Finch family ran the business and their descendants established the museum in 1966. The site was formerly used

The manganese-mill waterwheel at Morwellham Quay, Devon.

as a corn mill and woollen mill. There are three working wheels; one operates a pair of tilt hammers. There are a picnic area and refreshment kiosk. Tourist information point. Open: Easter to October, Monday to Saturday (plus Sundays June to September) 10-5. Party visits by arrangement. Contact: the Curator, Museum of Water Power, Finch Foundry, Sticklepath, Okehampton, Devon EX20 2NW (telephone: 0837 840046 or 52295).

Otterton Mill Centre, near Budleigh Salterton.
In Otterton village, off B3176 between Newton Poppleford and Budleigh Salterton.
   This mill was formerly owned by Otterton Priory. There are two breastshot Poncelet wheels. One has been restored to drive the machinery. Apart from the mill, visitors can see various craftsmen at work. Grinding takes place on three days each week and flour or bakery products can be purchased at the Barn Bakery. Open: April to December, daily 10.30-5.30; January to March, daily 11.30-4.30. Restaurant open daily from mid March to the end of October and on winter weekends. Audio-visual slide show. Contact: Desna Greenhow, Otterton Mill, near Budleigh Salterton, Devon EX9 7HG (telephone: 0395 68521 or 67041).

Parracombe Mill, Parracombe, Barnstaple.
   The 15 foot overshot wheel of this interesting mill is still in working order. It was last used to grind corn in 1945. Visitors are admitted by written appointment.

Riverside Mill, Bovey Tracey.
   This fine building is occupied by the Devon Guild of Craftsmen. It is open to the public as a museum of local crafts and holds exhibitions of craftwork. The waterwheel can be seen from the road bridge by the mill. Telephone: 0626 832223.

Town Mills, Clifford Street, Chudleigh.
   The Wheel Craft Workshops and restaurant occupy the mill premises where some of the machinery can still be seen. Visitors are welcome to walk through to see the large backshot waterwheel. The mill was mentioned in Domesday Book and was later one of many West Country mills involved in the woollen industry. It was later converted. Open: daily 10-5.30. Telephone: 0626 852698.

DORSET

Castleton Water Wheel, Sherborne.
On the eastern outskirts of the town.
   The waterwheel of the Castleton Waterworks has been restored

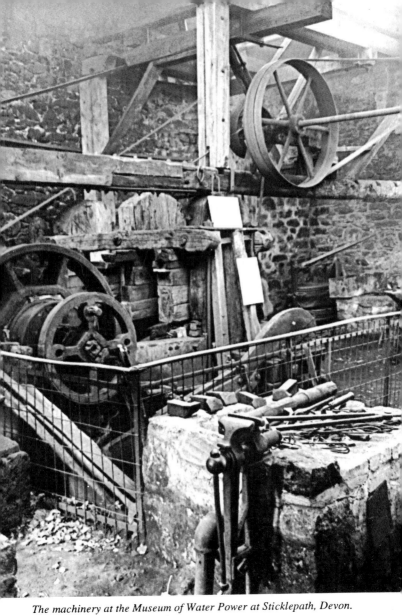

The machinery at the Museum of Water Power at Sticklepath, Devon.

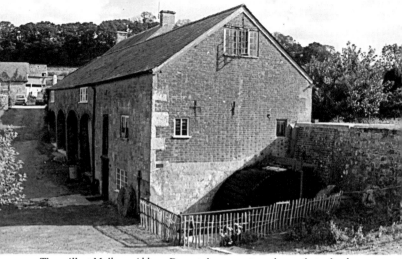

The mill at Melbury Abbas, Dorset, has an external overshot wheel.

by the Castleton Waterwheel Group. Group visits are welcome. Open as advertised locally or by arrangement with G. C. Bendell, 2 St Mary's Road, Sherborne, Dorset DT9 6DG (telephone: 0935 813598).

Mangerton Mill and Museum, Bridport.
Tourist sign off the A3066 Bridport to Beaminster road.
   The stone seventeenth-century building has an overshot wheel 12 feet in diameter by 4 feet wide. There are three pairs of stones, and animal food is produced. Its last miller retired in 1966 and the mill remained unused until the 1988 restoration. There was once a second wheel, which worked a flax mill. Open: 1st May to Spring Bank Holiday, 2.30-5.30; Easter week and Spring Bank Holiday to 30th September, 11-5.30; closed Mondays (except Bank Holidays). Museum of Rural Bygones; refreshments. Party visits by arrangement. Contact: Mr and Mrs Harris, Mangerton Mill, Mangerton, Bridport, Dorset DT6 3SG (telephone: 0308 85224).

Melbury Abbas Mill, Shaftesbury.
1½ miles south of Shaftesbury, between A350 and B3081.
   This mill on the river Sturkel has an external overshot wheel, 11 feet in diameter by 5 feet wide, and its original machinery. There are two pairs of Derbyshire stones. The three-storey mill is built of local Melbury stone. There is a Countryside Museum. Cream teas and stoneground flour are available. Open daily 10.30-5. Contact: J. Giles, Melbury Abbas Mill, Melbury Abbas, Shaftesbury, Dorset (telephone: 0747 52163).

Sturminster Newton Mill

Restored to full working order in 1981, this mill produces wholemeal flour and animal feed. A feature of the mill is its water turbine, which was installed in place of the traditional waterwheel in 1904. Open: May to September, Tuesday, Thursday and Saturday 11-5, Sunday 2-5. Party bookings: Mr B.M. Young, Whitecote, Manston Road, Sturminster Newton, Dorset DT10 1AG (telephone: 0258 72275).

The Water Mill, Upwey.

This working mill is Thomas Hardy's 'Overcombe Mill' in *The Trumpet Major*. Fresh wholemeal flour is always available. Open: Easter to September, Sunday, Monday, Thursday and Friday, 10.30-5; during July and August the mill is also open on Tuesday, Wednesday and Saturday 2-5. Parties by arrangement. Contact: the Manager, The Water Mill at Upwey, Church Street, Upwey, Weymouth, Dorset DT3 5QE (telephone: 0305 814233).

DURHAM

Killhope Lead Mining Centre, Upper Weardale.
Alongside the A689 Stanhope to Alston road.

This spectacular wheel, 33 feet 8 inches in diameter, is now turning again and is located at 1500 feet above sea level. The

At Sturminster Newton Mill in Dorset the waterwheel has been replaced by a water turbine.

The spectacular waterwheel at Killhope Lead Mining Centre in County Durham.

crushing mill and mine buildings have been restored. Work continues to re-establish the ore-dressing plant to its 1880 appearance. The visitor centre, at the best-preserved mine centre in England, contains an exhibition illustrating the life of the lead miners and their families. Open: Easter to October, daily, and Sundays in November, 10.30-5. Group bookings from November to March by arrangement. Coaches by appointment. Contact: Ian Forbes, Killhope Lead Mining Centre, Cowshill, County Durham DL13 1AR (telephone: 0388 537505 or 091-383 4144).

Mining sites have their own special dangers. Visitors should observe warning notices and not venture into old workings.

Leap Mill, Burnopfield.

This small corn mill has an overshot wheel which operates two pairs of stones. There is a mill dam which forms an impressive waterfall. The mill last worked in the 1920s and is undergoing restoration. It is located on a farm which has a collection of rare breeds. Open: Easter to October, Sundays and Bank Holidays 2-6. Telephone: 0207 71375.

EAST SUSSEX

Bartley Mill, Frant.
In the Winn Valley, 3 miles from Tunbridge Wells, just off B2169.
Formerly a hop farm, the mill now produces organic wheat. There was a mill on this site in the thirteenth century. The mill has

an overshot wheel and organic flour is produced. There are a farm shop and tearooms. Open all the year. Party bookings by arrangement. Contact: Mr P. Garnham, Bartley Mill, Bells Yew Green, Frant, East Sussex (telephone: 0892 890372 or 0233 20181).

Michelham Priory, Upper Dicker.

The mill is in the grounds of the Priory, now in the care of the Sussex Archaeological Society. It has been fully restored and the machinery is mostly modern but is of medieval design. The iron pit wheel is eighteenth-century. The stones are French burr. Grinding takes place on Wednesday afternoons and at other times when demand for flour dictates. A mill has occupied the site since the fourteenth century. There is an exhibition of milling tools and equipment and illustrated display boards describe the milling process. According to local legend Thomas à Becket fell into the millpond when he was hunting. The house, which dates in parts from the thirteenth century, and extensive gardens are also open. Picnic area, restaurant and coffee/tea shop. Open: late March to October, daily 11-5.30. Group bookings by arrangement. Contact: the Administrator, Michelham Priory, Upper Dicker, Hailsham, East Sussex BN27 3QS (telephone: 0323 844224).

Park Mill, Bateman's, Burwash.

In the village of Burwash about half a mile south of A265.

The watermill stands in the grounds of Bateman's, Rudyard

The restored mill in the grounds of Michelham Priory, East Sussex.

Park Mill at Rudyard Kipling's former home, Bateman's, East Sussex.

Kipling's home from 1902 to 1936. Bateman's is a National Trust property. The mill has been extensively restored and given a new overshot wheel. In addition to the usual milling machinery, Kipling installed a water turbine to provide electricity. Park Mill is featured in several of Kipling's stories: *Puck of Pook's Hill, Rewards and Fairies* and *Below the Mill Dam.* Stoneground wholemeal flour is available for sale. Open: April to October, Saturday to Wednesday, 11-5.30; last admission 4.30; also open on Good Friday. Information from the Administrator, Bateman's, Burwash, East Sussex TN19 7DS (telephone: 0435 882302).

ESSEX

Bourne Mill, Colchester.
About a mile from the centre of Colchester by the Mersea road and the Bourne road.

The present building, dating from 1591, is a distinctive structure with delicately stepped Dutch gable-ends. In the nineteenth century the mill was converted from wool processing to corn grinding and was worked until 1935. It was presented anonymously to the National Trust in 1936. The 18 foot diameter overshot interior wheel has 64 buckets and is 5 feet wide. A descriptive leaflet is available which contains a detailed sectional drawing. Open: Sundays and Mondays of Bank Holiday weekends, and Tuesdays in July and August, 2-5.30. Telephone: 0206 572422.

Easterford Watermill, Swan Street, Kelvedon.

This mill is being restored. It has a working breast wheel and three pairs of stones. Milling ceased in 1930 and renovation began in 1981. It is hoped to resume milling in late 1993. There are three or four open days each year (Sunday afternoons). School and other parties by arrangement. Contact: Marjorie Thompson, Easterford Mill, Swan Street, Kelvedon, Essex CO5 9NG (telephone: 0376 571360).

GLOUCESTERSHIRE

Arlington Mill, Bibury.

Arlington Mill stands in a most attractive setting. A very long leat carried the water from the stream, higher up the valley, to create a head of water for the wheel. The row of weavers' cottages overlooks the race as it flows down to rejoin the main stream. Since 1966 the mill has been a museum. An immense wooden pit wheel, with compass arms, is *in situ*, but the rest of the original machinery was removed when the mill was used in conjunction with a trout hatchery. The millstones on the first floor were installed in 1859 when the iron columns and fish-bellied girders were added to strengthen the structure. Other working machinery came from North Cerney Mill and this is operated by an electric motor which turns the pit wheel. Open: March to October, daily 10-7, or dusk if earlier. For winter opening times telephone for details. Parking in the village. Telephone: 0285 740368.

Dean Heritage Centre, Camp Mill, Soudley.
On B4227 between Cinderford and A48 at Blakeney.

This important site displays the agricultural and industrial history of the Forest of Dean. In 1986 a reproduction 12 foot diameter overshot wheel was installed in one of the wheelpits. This can be seen working. The present mill building dates from 1876. In 1888 it was converted to a leather-board mill making shoe insoles. It became a sawmill in 1911 and worked until 1952. There are many other aspects of forest life to explore at this well-presented museum. Open: April to October, daily 10-6; November to March, daily 10-5. Party visits by arrangement. Contact: Camp Mill, Soudley, Cinderford, Gloucestershire GL14 7AG (telephone: 0594 22170).

Lower Slaughter

The mill, set on the river Eye, now functions as a village bakery. The wide waterwheel is still in place and can be viewed from the riverside path which takes the visitor through the centre of this attractive Cotswold village.

Westington Mill, Chipping Campden.
At the west end of Chipping Campden, off Park Lane.

This privately owned mill ceased work as a corn mill in 1937. There are 5 acres of grounds and the millstream is a principal feature with its eight waterfalls. Many of the steps around the garden are made from old millstones which originated here and from mills at Evesham or Sedgeberrow. The garden is open sometimes (National Gardens Scheme).

GREATER MANCHESTER

Dunham Massey Sawmill
3 miles south-west of Altrincham, off A56.

Part of the National Trust estate at Dunham Massey Park, this was originally a corn mill. It was refitted as a sawmill about 1860 but became disused in 1895. It has now been restored by the Trust and a new overshot wheel drives the nineteenth-century machinery. The wooden wheel is 15 feet 4 inches in diameter and 3 feet wide. Via a wooden flywheel and lineshafting, it drives a large frame saw, a circular saw, a three-wheeled bandsaw, a boring machine, a crane and other items. Dunham Massey Park is open April to October (closed Good Friday); house, Saturday to Wednes-

The water-powered sawmill at the National Trust's property, Dunham Massey, south of Manchester.

day 12-5; garden, daily 12-5. The mill machinery will normally be open and operate on Wednesday and Sunday. Contact: Barbara Morley, National Trust Regional Office, Attingham Park, Shrewsbury, Shropshire SY4 4TP (telephone: 074377 343).

Portland Basin Industrial Heritage Centre, Ashton-under-Lyne.

This former canal warehouse, built in 1834, is situated on the Ashton/Peak Forest Canal and has a working 24 foot diameter waterwheel which provided power for the hoists. An exhibition illustrating the industrial and social history is open: April to September, Tuesday to Saturday 10-6, Sunday 12-6; October to March, Tuesday to Saturday 10-4, Sunday 12-4; also open on Bank Holiday Mondays. Party visits by arrangement. Contact: C. O'Mahony, Portland Basin Heritage Centre, Portland Street South, Ashton-under-Lyne, Lancashire OL6 7SY (telephone: 061-308 3374).

Tonge Moor Textile Museum, Bolton.

At an early stage in the industrial revolution water power was applied to textile manufacture. One of the significant innovations was Richard Arkwright's water frame (1769), which made possible the continuous spinning of thread. An example of an Arkwright frame is among this museum's collection. Open: Monday and Thursday 2-7.30, Tuesday and Friday 9.30-5.30, Saturday 9.30-12.30; closed Wednesday and Sunday. Contact: R.J. Bradbury, Human History Section, Bolton Museum and Art Gallery, Civic Centre, Bolton BL1 1SE (telephone: 0204 22311, extension 2195).

HAMPSHIRE

Alderholt Mill, Fordingbridge.

The mill stands on a tributary of the Avon, which forms the boundary between Hampshire and Dorset. A mill was recorded on this site in the fourteenth century and a mill was still worked here in 1945. After restoration the mill began work again in 1987. The present exterior wheel replaces one which was inside. It was built by Munden of Ringwood and dates from c.1840. Milling takes place on Sunday afternoons or by appointment. Open: Easter to September and mid November to Christmas, Tuesday, Friday and Sunday 2-6, Saturdays and Bank Holidays 10-6. Groups by appointment mornings and evenings. School parties welcome — guided tours and demonstration milling. All the renovation has been achieved by public support and with the help of local craftsmen and artists who display and sell their work. Contact: J. L. and L. A. Pye, Alderholt Mill, Sandleheath Road, Alderholt, Fordingbridge, Hampshire SP6 1PU (telephone: 0425 653130).

The tide mill at Eling near Totton, Hampshire.

Eling Tide Mill
South of A35 and on the north side of Bartley Water. Signposted from the A35 Totton bypass.

Bartley Water was dammed in the fifteenth century to provide a store of water for the mill's operation. When the tide rises it is allowed to pass through the mill sluice, where it is stored when the tide recedes. Each tide provides enough power for about four hours working. Eling is the only productive tide mill in western Europe. (The mill at Carew in Dyfed is used for demonstration purposes.) Eling Mill had two wheels of the Poncelet type and one has been restored. It operates a pair of stones which are regularly worked. The visitor can see a video film which explains the way in which a tide mill works. In addition to the machinery there is an interesting interpretative display. On the ground floor a glazed panel allows the wheel to be seen in motion. There is also a particularly fine miller's desk. Outside the mill the walk across the causeway shows the extent of the millpond and its associated sluices. Flour is regularly on sale. Open throughout the year, Wednesday to Sunday 10-4. Regular demonstrations. Parties by arrangement at any time. Contact: Martin Mears, Eling Tide Mill, Eling Toll Bridge, Eling, Totton, Southampton SO4 4HF (telephone: 0703 569575).

Headley Watermill, Bordon.
8 miles north of Petersfield.

The millers J. Ellis & Sons operate this commercial watermill to produce wholemeal flour and animal feed. Four pairs of stones are powered by a breastshot waterwheel supplied by a 4 acre millpond.

Paultons Park, Ower.

The watermill here is a sawmill. It fell into disuse about 1945. The wheel, built about 1860, is a Poncelet breastshot wheel, 15 feet in diameter, with 56 buckets. It was used to drive a racksaw bench for cutting timber from the old Paultons Estate. In 1982 the wheel was renovated and all 56 buckets were replaced. This involved removing and refitting over a thousand bolts. The frame of the wheel is made of cast iron and the buckets are steel. The wooden teeth of the drive wheels are made from the hornbeam which can be seen growing by the side of the mill. The wheel, driven by water from Paultons Lake, in turn drives a racksaw, similar to the original saw. Paultons Park is a family leisure park offering a day out for everyone. The waterwheel is one of over forty attractions. Open: March to October, daily from 10 o'clock. For full details telephone: 0703 814455. Contact: Paultons Park, Ower, Romsey, Hampshire SO51 6AL.

Whitchurch Silk Mill
Tourist signs from A34.

This mill has considerable technical importance as it retains its old power looms and winding and warping gear which are worked by the restored 1890 waterwheel. The Silk Mill is situated on Frog

The metal waterwheel at Paultons Park has been restored and now drives a racksaw for cutting timber.

Whitchurch Silk Mill in Hampshire still produces silk on its water-powered looms.

Island in the river Test and is the last working silk mill in the south of England. The mill exterior (*c.*1800) is brick but the interior walls are constructed of chalkstone. The mill still produces silk for academic gowns and other special purposes. Open: Tuesday to Sunday and Bank Holidays 10.30-5; closed between Christmas and New Year. The looms are not worked on Sundays. Group bookings by prior arrangement. Contact: Mrs C. S. Petter, Visitor Manager, Whitchurch Silk Mill, 28 Winchester Street, Whitchurch, Hampshire RG28 7AL (telephone: 0256 892065 or 893882).

Winchester City Mill
1 Water Lane, Winchester. On the Itchen north of Soke Bridge (A272).

Some machinery remains. This National Trust property is leased to the Youth Hostels Association. Open: April to September, daily except Mondays (but open Bank Holiday Mondays) 10-5; last admission 4.45. There is a shop. Public car park 100 yards. Contact: the Custodian, Winchester City Mill, Bridge Street, Winchester, Hampshire (telephone: 0962 870057).

HEREFORD AND WORCESTER

Churchill Forge, Churchill.
At the north-east end of the village on the Ganlar Brook. 'Foot-path to Stakenbridge' sign indicates the track leading to the forge.

This factory, which probably had its origins before the eighteenth century, is an important survivor of the early industrial era. There is a 2 acre hammer pond which stores water for the two wheels. The overshot wheel (17 feet by 5 feet 3 inches wide) has been restored. This also carries a spur gear which operates, via shafting, hammers, presses, etc. A crank on the outside end of the axle operates shears. The second, older wheel (17 feet by 2 feet 3 inches wide) has, unusually, seven spokes and was used for the furnace blower and grindstones. Edge tools, spades and single-piece ladles were manufactured in this forge, which worked until 1969. The Churchill Forge Trust is slowly restoring the premises, which provide a significant reference for industrial archaeologists, local historians and schools. There is an informative guidebook. There are several open days each year. Parties and individuals are admitted by arrangement. Contact: Mrs P. Hayward, Churchill Forge House, Churchill, Kidderminster, Worcestershire (telephone: 0562 700476).

Forge Mill Needle Museum, Redditch.

Forge Mill was converted from iron refining to needlemaking c.1730. It consists of two wings, between which is the wheel that originally worked the machinery in both wings. Water power was used for needle scouring (polishing) until 1958. From then it was cared for by volunteers until 1979, when the Redditch Amenity Trust was formed to restore the buildings and furnish them as a

Forge Mill in Redditch houses an exhibition of needlemaking.

museum. This was opened by the Queen in 1983. The wheel is an overshot bucket wheel, 14 feet 6 inches in diameter and 10 feet wide. There are eighty buckets and on load it would run at 6-12 revolutions per minute, generating around 37 horsepower. There is a good guidebook. Picnic area, museum shop. The Bordesley Abbey Visitor Centre, next to the Forge Mill, has displays which interpret finds from the twelfth-century Cistercian abbey. This is a very attractive site. Open: Easter to October, Monday to Thursday 11-4.30 (closed Fridays), Saturday 2-5, Sunday and Bank Holidays 11-5. Contact: Barry Mead, Forge Mill Museum, Needle Mill Lane, Redditch B97 6RR (telephone: 0527 62509).

Mortimer's Cross Mill, Lucton.

This eighteenth-century sandstone building on three floors with an undershot wheel was last worked in the 1940s. Open: April to September, Thursdays 12-5. Information: Historic Buildings and Monuments Commission, 15/17 Great Marlborough Street, London W1V 1AF (telephone: 071-734 6010).

Newnham Mill, Newnham Bridge.

Near the junction of A456 and A443 about 3 miles east of Tenbury Wells.

This small brick eighteenth-century mill is on the river Rea. There is an external wooden undershot wheel 15 feet in diameter and 5 feet wide with 26 paddles or floats. The wheel is worked by a 6 foot head of water and was used to pump water to the nearby Home Farm. In the early nineteenth century there were two wheels, but they were replaced by the existing wheel in 1837. The machinery was renovated in 1928, when the present cast-iron pit wheel and wallower were installed. There are three pairs of stones and appropriate ancillary machinery. Newnham Mill was worked during the Second World War but later fell into disuse. It was restored to working order in 1978. This is one of the few commercially operating watermills. It is open for flour sales, but viewing is by appointment only. Contact: Robert Higginson, Newnham Mill, Newnham Bridge, Tenbury Wells, Worcestershire WR15 8JE (telephone: 058479 494).

HERTFORDSHIRE

Kingsbury Watermill, St Michael's Street, St Albans.

The mill is Elizabethan in origin and is scheduled as an ancient monument. It was in use until 1936 and restored in 1973 as a museum with a working waterwheel and a collection of farming and milling implements. The wheel is undershot and the machinery is mostly nineteenth-century. Open: Tuesday to Saturday, 11-

Kingsbury Watermill in St Albans is also a craft centre and restaurant.

6, Sunday 12-6; November to March, closes at 5; closed Mondays (except Bank Holidays) and from 25th December to 2nd January. Restaurant and art/craft centre open at the same times. Parties at any time of the year on application. Telephone: 0727 53502.

Mill Green Mill and Museum, Hatfield.
At the junction of A414 and A1000, signposted.

Part of Welwyn Hatfield Museum Service, the mill house contains local history displays. The mill, once known as Hatfield Mill, is fully restored. It has a low breastshot wheel and two pairs of French burr stones. Milling takes place on Tuesday, Wednesday

Mill Green Mill and Museum regularly mills its own flour for sale.

and/or Sunday and is subject to demand for flour and weather conditions. Telephone to confirm before making a visit. A very well-produced guidebook explains the working and history of the mill. Flour is sold on site. Open: Tuesday to Friday 10-5, weekends and Bank Holidays 2-5. Craft demonstrations and other special events each weekend from May to September. Group bookings by arrangement. Contact: Mill Green Museum, Mill Green, Hatfield, Hertfordshire AL9 5PD (telephone: 0707 271362).

ISLE OF MAN

Lady Isabella Wheel, Laxey.

This is a great tourist attraction, and each year thousands of visitors climb the 95 steps to its upper platform. It was built in 1854 to pump water from the deep Laxey mines and it was working until

1929. This pitchback wheel makes two and a half turns a minute and used to generate 185 horsepower. It has a diameter of 72 feet 6 inches and is 6 feet wide. Each one of its 168 buckets can hold 24 gallons. The axle is 17 feet long, 21 inches in diameter and weighs 9 tons. The Lady Isabella Wheel was designed by the engineer Robert Casement and was named after the wife of the island's governor. It is now owned by the Isle of Man Government, and it is open at Easter and then from May to September. Details of the opening times may be obtained from the Tourist Information Centre, 13 Victoria Street, Douglas, Isle of Man (telephone: 0624 74323).

ISLE OF WIGHT

Blackgang Chine, Chale.

In this spectacular setting a theme park illustrating the World of Timber has been created. The exhibition includes a reconstruction of a water-powered sawmill. A launder carries the water to the 14 foot diameter breastshot wheel. Open: April, May, late September and early October, daily 10-5; June to mid September, daily 10-10. Telephone: 0983 730330.

Calbourne Watermill and Museum of Rural Life

Half a mile west of Calbourne on B3401.

This restored seventeenth-century mill has a 20 foot overshot wheel with 48 buckets. At work it required about 3900 gallons of water a minute, or more than 1000 tons an hour. A calculation in

Calbourne Watermill on the Isle of Wight.

the guidebook states that each pound of meal produced used 225 gallons of water. In addition to the traditional millstones there are some late Victorian roller machines. A second 9 foot wheel can be seen in the grounds. The hollow-post wind engine, built for the Liverpool Garden Festival, is also part of the permanent exhibits. The rural bygones collection portrays agricultural implements, wagons and domestic life. Outside there is a spare waterwheel — a unique feature! Picnic area; refreshments. Open: Easter to 1st November, daily 10-6. Telephone: 098378 227.

Yafford Mill and Farm Park
Signposted half a mile south-west of Shorwell, on B3399.

This corn mill was operational until 1970 and has now been restored to its working state. Tools and other equipment relating to milling are on exhibition. In addition there are a nature trail, farm museum and picnic area. Open: Easter to October, daily 10-6. Telephone: 0983 740610 or 68431.

KENT

Chart Mills, Faversham.
Reached from West Street via Westbrook Walk or from South Road via Nobel Court.

There were originally four gunpowder mills on this site. One mill has been mostly restored and the stone beds of the other three have been excavated. The restored mill has a pair of 3 ton edge runners which were used for mixing (incorporating) the sulphur, saltpetre and charcoal. In use the process of incorporation lasted for many hours. The quality of the powder was determined by the length of the mixing time. For demonstration purposes a special simulated but inert compound is used. There was probably a gunpowder mill here in the sixteenth century, but the present building, the oldest of its kind in the world, dates from the 1760s. At that time the manufacture of powder was nationalised because private suppliers were producing an inferior product. With the end of the Napoleonic Wars the factory reverted to private ownership. The exterior lies on a public right of way and is always on view. Chart Mills are the only surviving gunpowder mills in Britain. Open: Easter to October, Sunday and Bank Holidays 2.30-5. Group bookings by arrangement. Information from: Honorary House Manager, Fleur de Lis Heritage Centre, Preston Street, Faversham, Kent ME13 8NS (telephone: 0795 534542). The Centre is open Mondays to Saturdays, except Thursdays.

Crabble Corn Mill, Lower Road, Dover.
This mill, on the river Dour, represents an important part of the

Chart Mills, Faversham, Kent, is the oldest gunpowder mill in the world and was nationalised during the Napoleonic Wars. It was restored by the Faversham Society.

Crabble Mill in Dover still has the grading machinery for producing an improved quality of white flour.

town's technical and commercial history. Built *c.*1812, it has been altered at different times and is now a significant building with six floors. There is a large breast wheel which was formerly enclosed. It worked until 1893 and has now been rebuilt. Crabble Mill was probably built to provide flour for troops stationed in Dover Castle. In the 1860s flour from the mill was regularly shipped to London. About a decade later new sieving machinery which produced a better grade of white flour was installed. The mill has a complete set of grading machinery for this purpose *in situ*. Stoneground wholemeal flour is still sold at the mill. There are a shop, a cafeteria and a museum of milling history. Car park opposite the mill. Open at times throughout the year. For details of opening contact: Andrew Denyer, Crabble Corn Mill, Lower Road, River, Dover CT17 0UY (telephone: 0304 823292).

Swanton Mill, Mersham.

Standing on the East Stour river, the present mill (*c.*1610) occupies a Domesday site. With its brickwork, weatherboarding, granary and luccam (to hoist the sacks of corn), this mill presents a very attractive exterior within a tranquil setting. In 1975 the careful restoration work was recognised by a Civic Trust Award. There is a 6 foot 8 inch diameter overshot wheel, which is 8 feet 4 inches wide. There are French burr and Peak stones. Flour was ground here until the 1920s. This is a listed Grade II (starred) building of special historic interest. Organic wholemeal flour and refreshments are on sale. Open: April to September, Saturday and Sunday 3-6. Contact: Mrs Gay Christiansen (for party and out-of-season visits), 18 Kensington Square, London W8 5HH (telephone: 0233 720223 or 071-937 0931).

LANCASHIRE

Helmshore Textile Museums
Holcombe Road, Helmshore.

This complex includes a water-powered fulling mill constructed in 1789. The present high breastshot waterwheel was installed in about 1850 and restored in 1978. It is approximately 18 feet in diameter and 11 feet wide overall, power being transmitted via two rim gears. Fulling is a finishing process for woollen cloth, and five pairs of fulling stocks contemporary with the wheel, as well as other early wool-finishing machines, can be seen. An adjacent nineteenth-century condenser cotton-spinning mill houses a museum of the Lancashire Textile Industry, which contains much early twentieth-century machinery. There is also a textile exhibi-

Swanton Mill, Kent, has a luccam to hoist sacks of grain.

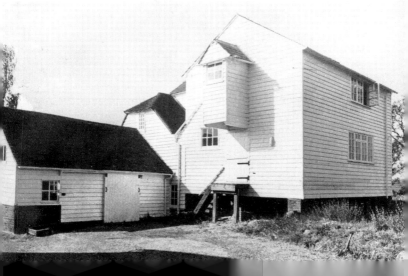

tion gallery. Two mill buildings, three reservoirs and a remote chimney make an interesting industrial complex. Parties can book a guided tour. Cafeteria. Details of opening arrangements may be obtained from Higher Mill Museum, Holcombe Road, Helmshore, Rossendale, Lancashire (telephone: 0706 226459).

Turton Tower
Off Chapeltown Road, Turton, near Bolton.
    The tower is a historic fifteenth-century house built in the style of a pele tower. It is owned by Lancashire County Council. In the tower grounds, on a site open to the public at all times, is the waterwheel from Blackrock Cotton Mill at Turton Bottoms. This wheel (*c.*1830) was restored in 1978 when it was placed in its present position. When funds allow, a water supply will be provided to turn it. For information, telephone: 0204 852203.

The Water Wheel Restaurant, Chipping.
    This superbly restored eighteenth-century corn mill is located in one of Lancashire's most attractive villages. The waterwheel can still be seen turning in the brookside gardens. Open during business hours; closed Sunday evenings and Mondays. Contact: Mr Wareing, The Water Wheel Restaurant, Chipping, near Preston, Lancashire (telephone: 0995 553).

LINCOLNSHIRE

Alvingham Mill, Church Lane, Alvingham.
Close to the site of Alvingham Priory, about 3¹/₂ miles north-east of Louth, reached by unclassified roads.
    This is a working mill. The waterwheel is 11 feet in diameter and 8 feet wide and most of the machinery is cast iron. At present one pair of Derbyshire Peak stones is in use and grinding takes place on each open day. Open: August and September, second and fourth Sunday of the month, 2-4.30; Monday and Thursday 2-5; Bank Holidays (not Saturday) 11-5. Parties by arrangement. Telephone: 050782 554.

Claythorpe Watermill, Aby.
    This eighteenth-century listed mill is set in the Lincolnshire Wolds. The mill workings have been restored. Restaurant. Parties by arrangement. Contact: Claythorpe Watermill, Aby, Alford, Lincolnshire (telephone: 0521 50687).

Cogglesford Mill, Sleaford.
Off the A153 on the eastern side of Sleaford.
    This eighteenth-century mill on the river Slea was given to

North Kesteven District Council in 1990. The council have since completely restored the building and the machinery with its three sets of stones to working order. Exhibition. Open: May to September, Monday to Friday 10-4, Saturday and Sunday 1-4; October to April, Saturday and Sunday 12-4. Contact: Tourist Information Centre, telephone: 0529 414294.

Stockworth Mill, near Somersby.

This mill has distinct associations with the poet Alfred Tennyson, who wrote about it in *The Miller's Daughter*. The unusual wheel has an iron centre and rim but wooden spokes. The mill is now a craft centre and tearoom.

LONDON

Merton Abbey Mills, Watermill Way, London SW19 2RD.
Opposite the Savacentre car park.

The wheelhouse and wheel of the former Liberty Mills have been restored and now form part of a Craft Village. There is a spectacular 12 foot 6 inch diameter wheel which has several interesting features. It is 10 feet 4 inches wide, and its open paddles are supported on four sets of spokes, rims and hubs. Each spoked section is cast in one piece. Each hub has an octagonal profile which provided the pattern maker with an unusual geometrical problem when seven spokes had to be made to fit around the centre. The floats are 14 inches wide and make the wheel's outside diameter almost 15 feet. Inside the building there is a 12 foot 2 inch diameter spur wheel which operated the mill's former machinery. Open weekends. Coach and school parties by arrangement. Telephone: 081-543 9608. Fax: 081-540 1145.

NORFOLK

Bintree Mill

This four-storeyed mill with pantiled roof is on the river Wensum. There are an attractive bridge over the millpond and some interesting gear controlling the bypass sluice.

Gunton Park Sawmill, Gunton Park.
About 5 miles south of Cromer between A140 and A149, Gunton Park may be approached via the minor road that leaves A140 just south of Hanworth Cross. About half a mile from the main road the gatehouse can be seen on the left-hand side. Passing through the gate a public right of way provides an approach to the hall. A short distance from the gateway the track divides. Take the right-hand trackway. The sawmill can be approached through the woodland.

The headrace and paddles to control the water at Gunton Park Sawmill. The left-hand gate has its levers in position. The thatched mill has been restored by local societies.

It is at the eastern edge of the wood beside a stream.

The sawmill is a timber-framed thatched building. The water supply comes from the ornamental lake in the park. There were originally two waterwheels and one survives. There is an ancient reciprocating saw, which is mounted in a heavy wooden framework that is not part of the building's structure. The momentum of the saw is maintained by a very large flywheel (about 6 feet 6 inches in diameter). A crankshaft fixed to the flywheel has its connecting rod attached to the actual saw frame, which moves up and down. Several blades can be placed in the saw frame and the thickness of the timber being worked can be varied. The timber is mounted on a carriage which moves on rails. At each stroke of the saw the carriage advances. The mechanism probably dates from *c.*1800 and it therefore has considerable technical importance. The Norfolk Mills and Pumps Trust, which has a long lease on the mill, has in conjunction with the Norfolk Industrial Archaeological Society restored the mill to full working order. Sawing demonstrations take place on the days indicated below, but special arrangements can be made for groups at other times. Open: the fourth Sunday in each month from April to September, 2-5. Contact: Technical Adviser, Norfolk Mills and Pumps Trust, County Hall, Martineau Lane, Norwich, Norfolk NR1 2DH (telephone: 0603 222705).

Letheringsett Watermill, Holt.

One mile west of Holt off A418. Follow tourist signs.

This brick mill, built in 1802 on a Domesday site, has an undershot wheel which works two sets of stones. It is a working mill producing flour for sale. There are a shop and museum. Guided tours are provided on milling days, Tuesday, Thursday and Sunday, 2-4.30. Wholewheat flour is produced from locally grown crops. Open: all year, Tuesday to Friday 9-1, 2-5; Saturday 9-1; also Sundays from Spring Bank Holiday to first week in September, 2-4.30. Party visits by prior arrangement at non-milling times. Member of the Guild of Master Craftsmen. Contact: M. D. Thurlow, Letheringsett Watermill, Riverside Road, Letheringsett, Holt, Norfolk NR25 7YD (telephone: 0263 713153).

Letheringsett Watermill, Norfolk, is a working mill with a shop and a museum.

Little Cressingham Wind and Watermill
About 2 miles west of Watton, just off B1108.

The mill is a combined wind and watermill. Two pairs of stones on the first floor were driven by power from the waterwheel and two on the third floor were driven by wind. Having fallen into disrepair, the mill was taken into the care of the Norfolk Mills and Pumps Trust in 1981 and is gradually being restored. In addition to the milling machinery, there are a Bramah pump and hydraulic ram, both of which were used to supply water to the gardens of Clermont Lodge. There are two waterwheels. The breastshot mill wheel is 12 feet by 6 feet wide. An 8 foot by 3 foot wide high-breast wheel drives the Bramah pump. The Trust has spent several years restoring the wheels and pump house. Major repairs to the corn mill will begin in 1994. It is hoped to demonstrate the Bramah pump, which provided water to Clermont Lodge gardens, by re-creating the millpond in 1993. Seats have been provided at the mill, which is in a delightful setting. Open: May to October, Sundays 2-5, or by appointment. Contact: Mr E. Apling, Church Cottage, Woodrising, Norfolk NR9 4PJ (telephone: 0953 850567).

Snettisham Mill.
Off Station Road, Snettisham. Tourist sign on A149 11 miles from King's Lynn.

The mill on the river Ingol was built by subscription in 1800 at a cost of £800. Poor people could have their corn ground here at four pence a bushel. A stone tablet records that the mill was 'erected in a time of scarcity'. Flour was produced until 1936. Purchased by the present owners in 1981, the mill was restored to working order in 1984. It has a high-breast wheel 14 feet 6 inches in diameter by 5 feet 3 inches wide. At a speed of five revolutions a minute the wheel generates about 9 horsepower. The cast-iron wheel has a gear ring on one side which operates a spur wheel on the main shaft. This is an unusual arrangement in a corn mill. Two pairs of stones are driven from above via a stone nut and quant. A pair of underdrift stones (not operational) are situated on the bin floor. Detailed guide/history. Party visits by arrangement. Open: 15th July to 9th September, Thursday and Bank Holiday Sunday/Monday, 10-5.30. Contact: R. E. Nott, The Mill House, Snettisham, King's Lynn, Norfolk PE31 7QJ (telephone: 0485 542180).

NORTHAMPTONSHIRE

Ashton Wold, near Oundle.

The mill was rebuilt by the first Lord Rothschild in 1900 from a former corn and fulling mill to provide electricity and a water supply to Ashton Wold. Drinking water was also laid on to the

Billing Mill in Northamptonshire.

estate houses. Blackstone diesel engines supplemented the water turbines. There is a bygones museum with agricultural and craft tools. Open throughout the year, every Sunday 2-6. For information, telephone: 0832 73575.

Billing Mill, Little Billing.
Part of Billing Aquadrome.

This mill has been restored to working order. The structure dates from the early years of the nineteenth century. Among its interesting features is the large iron waterwheel with, unusually, six spokes and open paddles. Visitors can see the mill working in April and May, weekends only, 12-6; June to August, daily, 12-6. There are facilities for refreshments. Telephone: 0604 408181.

NORTHUMBERLAND

Ford Forge, Heatherslaw Mill, Ford.

The existing building probably dates from the eighteenth century, with nineteenth-century alterations. It is really two mills under one roof. There are two wheels, 16 feet 8 inches by 5 feet wide, which each drive three pairs of stones, plus another vertical stone for pearl barley. In the nineteenth century much oatmeal was produced as well as flour. In those days it was the 'batcher', the miller carter, who brought the labourers' corn to be ground. The miller's toll for grinding was known as 'mouter'. During the 1940s mill hands worked a fifty-hour week. There were two shifts, from 7 am to 5 pm and from 5 pm to 3.30 am, an arrangement which kept the mill at work for twenty hours each day. The north granary now serves as a café. Craft shop. Wholemeal flour and other cereal products are on sale at the mill. Flour is supplied to local bakers and shops. There are daily demonstrations. Group bookings — minimum ten. Open: Easter to October, daily 10-6; winter weekends 1-4. Contact: Mr F. Waters, Heatherslaw Mill Trust, Ford and Etal Estates, Ford Village, Berwick-on-Tweed, Northumberland TD12 4TJ.

Warton Farm Waterwheel, Cragside House, Rothbury.

As part of the restoration project to reinstate the first Lord Armstrong's hydro-electric system, Warton Farm's wheel has been refurbished. It dates from after 1850 and it also provided the farm with a domestic water supply. This wheel marks the site of Cragside's new Power Circuit walk which includes the Ram and Power Houses. Cragside, now a National Trust property, was the first house in the world to be lit by hydro-power. Country park and garden open: April to October, daily (but closed Mondays except Bank Holidays) 10.30-7; November and December, Tuesday, Saturday and Sunday 10.30-4.

NORTH YORKSHIRE

The Corn Mill, Stamford Bridge.

This eighteenth-century five-storey mill is now a restaurant. The wheel can be seen working from one of the bars. It is an undershot metal wheel, installed in 1923 by Hawksheads of Yarm, and weighs 20 tons.

Crakehall Watermill, Little Crakehall.

By the bridge over Crakehall Beck on the A684 Bedale to Leyburn road.

There was a mill on this site before the Domesday survey of 1086. The present mill worked until 1927. This small seventeenth-century manorial mill has a low-breast wheel 15 feet in diameter by 5 feet wide with forty buckets. The present wheel was made, c.1860, by F. Mattison of Bedale. Four pairs of stones worked two Derbyshire grits and two French burrs. The latter pair are still in use. Stoneground wholemeal flour is produced throughout the year, and it is sold at the mill as well as in the surrounding area. Crakehall Mill is in a delightful setting. Open: Easter to September, Tuesday, Wednesday, Thursday, Saturday, Sunday and Bank Holidays 10-5. Tearoom. Parties by arrangement. Contact: Peter

Townsend, The Mill House, Little Crakehall, near Bedale, North Yorkshire DL8 1HU (telephone: 0677 423240).

York Castle Museum

Among the many delights to be seen in this superb museum is the Raindale Corn Mill, which came from the North Yorkshire Moors near Pickering. Its external overshot wheel works a single pair of stones. The museum is open: November to March, Monday to Saturday 9.30-5, Sunday 10-5; April to November, Monday to Saturday 9.30-6.30, Sunday 10-6.30; last admission one hour before closing. Contact: York Castle Museum, York YO1 1RY (telephone: 0904 653611). Group bookings, telephone: 0904 633932 (weekdays 2-4.30).

OXFORDSHIRE

Combe Mill, Combe, near Woodstock.
On the Windrush, below Combe station.

The iron Victorian waterwheel, 12 feet in diameter by 8 feet wide, survives with the necessary gearing. It worked the Duke of Marlborough's sawmill. In 1852 water power was supplemented by the installation of a beam engine. This engine with its contemporary boiler has been carefully restored, and it is in steam on each open day. Open third Sunday in May, August and October. Contact: M. J. Hallam, Dornford Ridge, Burditch Bank, Wootton-by-Woodstock, Oxford OX20 1EH (telephone: 0993 811118).

Mapledurham House, Mapledurham.
Signposted off A4074 (Reading-Oxford) at the Pack Saddle public house.

This restored mill stands close to Mapledurham House, a fine Elizabethan mansion, and the interesting parish church. The mill has been carefully restored since 1977 and once again grinds corn. Visitors can see the working mill in motion on open days. The external undershot wheel is quite spectacular. It drives two pairs of French stones. Open: Easter to September, Saturday, Sunday and Bank Holiday Mondays 1-5. The riverside picnic park opens at 12.30 on open days. Midweek group visits by appointment throughout the year. School parties welcome. Contact: Miss J. R. Emary, The Estate Office, Mapledurham, Reading RG4 7TR (telephone: 0734 723350; fax: 0734 724016).

Venn Mill, Garford.
On the west side of A338 from Cumnor to Wantage, 2 miles south of Frilford, where the Childrey Brook passes beneath the road; clearly named on the latest Ordnance Survey maps.

Venn Mill at Garford in Oxfordshire was built at the beginning of the nineteenth century.

The existing mill and its machinery were constructed *c*.1800 and its features reflect the rustic ingenuity of the period. Its undershot wheel is 13 feet 5 inches in diameter by 5 feet 9 inches wide. Venn Mill ceased work about 1940 and was subsequently used for non-milling purposes. Wholemeal flour is ground on the second Sunday in each month from May to October, 10-5, and at other times by arrangement. Contact: Alan Stoyel, The Old School House, Stanford-in-the-Vale, Faringdon, Oxfordshire SN7 8LH (telephone: 0367 718888).

SHROPSHIRE

Chadwell Mill, Chadwell, near Newport.
About half a mile off A41 and 4 miles from Newport.

Chadwell Mill is an eighteenth-century working corn mill producing stoneground wholemeal flour, which is available for sale. A 23 foot diameter iron-rimmed overshot waterwheel with oak spokes and buckets drives two pairs of French burr stones of 4 foot 9 inch diameter. The mill, which is fully restored, is very unusual; the mill pool is spring-fed from the site of St Chad's Well and the waterwheel used to power machinery via a steel rope drive to a neighbouring farm some 400 yards away. The same water that drives the watermill also supplies a large part of the locality with drinking water. The existing mill is the last of many mills to have been on this site, and in the eighteenth century a forge was incorporated to produce ships' anchors. The old brick-built wagon shed has been converted into tearooms where the flour is used to produce scones and cakes. The mill is open but check times before visiting (telephone: 095270 578).

Daniel's Mill, Eardington (*see cover picture*).
Near the Severn Valley Railway half a mile from the junction of the Highley (B4555) and Cleobury Mortimer (B4363) roads from Bridgnorth. Follow brown tourist signs.

This attractive mill is in a fine setting and it has one special feature which sets it apart from other corn mills. Its spectacular 38 foot diameter wheel, the largest operating a corn mill, was working until 1957. There are three pairs of French burr stones. After restoration the mill is again operating and stoneground flour can be purchased. Gift shop. Refreshments. Exhibitions of bygones and old country tools. Parties by arrangement at any time of year. Open: Easter to September, Saturday, Sunday and Bank Holidays 11-6. Contact: Alan and Joyce George, Daniel's Mill, Eardington, Bridgnorth, Shropshire WV16 5JL (telephone: 0746 762753).

SOMERSET

Combe House Hotel, Holford.
The 26 foot wheel here dates from 1893. It formerly worked, at different times, a tannery pump, a sawmill, a generator, a stone breaker and a chaff cutter. Telephone: 027874 382.

Cutterne Mill, Evercreech, Shepton Mallet.
Just off A371 between Shepton Mallet and Castle Cary.

There has been a mill on this site since 1086, when rent was paid to the Bishop of Wells. The present building dates from 1628 and most of the machinery from 1862. The pit, spur and crown wheels and the waterwheel are all metal and the rusted buckets of the high breastshot waterwheel have all been recently replaced to allow the wheel to run. It was a grist mill, predominantly for cattle fodder using Russian barley shipped via Bristol docks, and was operated up to 1932. There are displays on corn milling. Although this mill is no longer open to the public, private visitors are admitted by appointment. Contact: M. Ralph (telephone: 0749 830331).

Dunster Mill, Mill Lane, Dunster.
The mill (*c.*1680) is situated on the river Avill below Dunster Castle. It has a picturesque setting and an interesting but much rebuilt exterior. The mill leat is almost a mile long and visitors can

view it and the wheels from a special observation platform. There
are two 12 foot overshot wheels of wood and iron which can be
worked together or alone. There are two gear trains and a total of
three pairs of French burr stones, one dated 1869. Wholemeal flour
is produced for visitors and local shops. Dunster is a working mill
and flour is always being ground. There is a collection of agricultural bygones on the first floor. Car parks 150 yards away at Park
Road or Dunster Castle. Open: April to June, daily (except Easter
Saturday) 11-5; July and August, daily 11-5; September and October, daily (except Saturday) 11-5.

Hornsbury Mill, Chard.
About a mile from Chard town centre on A358 to Ilminster.
   This interesting mill retains all its basic machinery and visitors
can clearly see how the grinding process was performed. There are
three pairs of underdriven stones. The spur wheel is 8 feet in
diameter. From the restaurant you can see the internal 18 foot
waterwheel, which has wooden spokes and an iron rim. The wheel
rotates at a speed of four to six revolutions each minute. Each of
the buckets can hold about 20 gallons of water. The mill also
contains a museum of bygones, the collection of Mr Austin Wookey.
Cream teas, lunches, bar. Open all year, Monday to Saturday 10
am to 11 pm. Coaches and large groups by appointment. Contact:
R. R. Cox, General Manager, Hornsby Mill, Eleighwater, Chard,
Somerset TA20 3AQ (telephone: 0460 63317).

*Visitors to Dunster Mill in Somerset can view the two waterwheels from
an observation platform.*

The vatman demonstrating the art of papermaking by hand at Wookey Hole paper mill.

Orchard Mill, Williton.
Just south of Williton. Turn left off the A39 Minehead road just after the junction with A358 from Taunton and pass Williton church. The mill is signposted across fields.

Although this seventeenth-century mill was a corn mill in the nineteenth century it once ground alabaster. There is a 17 foot diameter wheel, 4 feet wide. All the internal machinery remains and it is hoped to grind flour soon. Museum, tearooms and shop. Open: April to October, daily 10-6; November to March, daily 11-5. Information and party bookings: telephone 0984 32133.

Piles Mill, Allerford.
About a mile east of Porlock, off A39.

This small mill has an overshot wheel, but no original machinery. There is a collection of agricultural bygones. Open daily during the summer. Information and out-of-season visits on application to National Trust, Holnicote Estate Office, Selworthy, Minehead, Somerset (telephone: 0643 862452).

Wookey Hole
2 miles from Wells.

This site, famous for its caves, also has a working paper mill. The tradition of papermaking here dates from the seventeenth century. Visitors can watch all the papermaking processes as well as printing on a Common Press replica. The overshot waterwheel is a reminder of the power source used before steam was introduced in 1855. It was built in 1980, is 12 feet in diameter and 4 feet wide, and is fed by water from the caves via an original eighteenth-century leat. A modern hydro-electric turbine was installed in 1984. Picnic area. Restaurant. Open: March to October, daily 9.30-5.30; November to February, daily 10.30-4.30, closed 17th to 25th December inclusive. For information and party bookings contact: Wookey Hole Caves Ltd, Wookey Hole, Wells, Somerset BA5 1BB (telephone: 0749 672243).

SOUTH YORKSHIRE

Abbeydale Industrial Hamlet, Sheffield.
On Abbeydale Road South, the A621 Sheffield to Bakewell road, on the south-western side of Sheffield.
   The hamlet was one of the largest water-powered works on the river Sheaf and was operating from at least 1712 to 1933. Here were made, from raw materials to finished items, scythes, hay knives and agricultural edge tools. In 1935, two years after production ceased, the late Alderman J. G. Graves purchased the site and gave it to Sheffield Corporation. The buildings were later restored by the Council for the Conservation of Sheffield Antiquities and developed as an industrial museum, which was opened to the public in 1970. The complete process of manufacture of scythes can be seen here. The crucible steel furnace is of the type invented by Benjamin Huntsman in 1742. The tilt forge was built in 1785 and the grinding shop in 1817. There are four wheels. An 18 foot, 5 foot 6 inch wide backshot wheel generating 30 horsepower drives the 23 ton tilt hammers. The overshot blowing-engine wheel is 14 feet in diameter and 1 foot 10 inches wide. A similar wheel provides power to the boring shop. The grinding hull (workshop) wheel is of about the same dimensions as the tilt-forge wheel. As well as the manufacturing buildings there are a row of workers' cottages, the manager's house, the counting house and the Jessop tilt hammers from the old Brightside Works. Three of the wheels are usually in motion each day, depending on the water supply. Working days and demonstrations are advertised. Refreshments. Pre-booked parties welcome. Guided tours and evening visits by arrangement. One-day courses are held for teachers planning a visit. Open Monday to Saturday 10-5, Sunday 11-5. Information and bookings: Abbeydale Industrial Hamlet, Abbeydale Road South, Sheffield S7 2QW (telephone: 0742 367731).

Shepherd Wheel, Hangingwater Road, Sheffield.
   The location of this water-powered cutlery grinding mill is typical of the early industrial mills which are sited, often in remote

The tilt forge, built in 1785, is amongst the water-powered machinery on exhibition at Abbeydale Industrial Hamlet near Sheffield. The complete process of scythe manufacture can be followed in the museum.

Shepherd Wheel, Sheffield, was a cutlery grinding mill.

places, along suitable rivers. In contrast to Abbeydale, this mill performed one process. The two grinding hulls were powered by a single overshot wheel (17 feet by 6 feet) which turned the grindstones by a system of lineshafts and pulleys. Open: Wednesday to Saturday 10-5, Sunday 11-5; closed Mondays and Tuesdays (except Bank Holidays). Arrangements for party visits as Abbeydale Industrial Hamlet, above.

Worsbrough Mill Museum, Barnsley.
Off the A61 Barnsley to Sheffield road, 2 miles north of M1 junction 36.

Here is an early seventeenth-century watermill with an adjacent nineteenth-century steam-driven mill set in a 200 acre country park with open working farm and fishing reservoir. Both mills have been restored to working order and a range of stoneground flour is now produced on the restored machinery and sold along with souvenirs and other natural products at the mill shop. The mill site, farm and surrounding country park are owned and operated by Barnsley Metropolitan Borough Council. The watermill is worked daily and contains three pairs of stones driven by a 14 foot 4 inch diameter cast-iron overshot wheel. The nineteenth-century mill, now powered by a rare Hornsby hot-bulb oil engine, contains two further pairs of stones. Ancillary machines include an oat roller, a kibbler, a sack hoist and a separator. The mill is worked regularly and there is a programme of Bank Holiday milling days and special events in conjunction with Wigfield Farm. Visiting groups, and particularly disabled people, are welcome, with guided tours of each facility available on request. Open: March to October, Wednesday to Sunday 10-5; November to February, Wednesday to Sunday 10-4; closed Mondays, Tuesdays and Christmas period; open Bank Holiday Mondays. Group bookings by arrangement. Contact: the Curator, Worsbrough Mill Museum, Worsbrough Bridge, Barnsley, South Yorkshire S70 6LJ (telephone: 0226 774527).

Wortley Top Forge, Sheffield.
Between Deepcar and Thurgoland, close to Well Hill Road, Sheffield (grid reference SK 295999).
This is believed to be the only remaining ironworks of its kind in Britain still on its original site, and complete with dam, sluices, hammers and waterwheels. The forge was started in the early

Worsbrough Mill Museum, between Barnsley and Sheffield, has a cast-iron overshot wheel.

seventeenth century and made iron for nails. With the advent of railways, axles were made, but production ceased about 1908. There are three waterwheels. A 12 foot breastshot wheel cast in a single piece was used for a tilt hammer. A 13 foot 6 inch breastshot wheel was used for a similar purpose. A pitchback wheel with a cog ring to drive a layshaft formerly worked an axle test rig, a pump and a blower for the furnaces. Restoration by the South Yorkshire Trades Historical Trust. Open: Sundays 11-5. For information and party bookings telephone Mrs J. Clarke: 0742 882649.

STAFFORDSHIRE

Brindley Mill, Mill Street, Leek.

This mill has particular associations with James Brindley, the canal builder, who came to live here as a child. The mill houses a comprehensive Brindley exhibition. The present structure dates from 1752. The external waterwheel is 11 feet in diameter and has forty elm boards (paddles). All the necessary machinery is in working order. Stoneground flour is sometimes obtainable. Open: Easter to October, Saturday, Sunday and Bank Holidays 2-5; from third Monday in July to end of August, also open on Monday, Tuesday and Wednesday 2-5. Group bookings by arrangement with Tourist Information Centre, Market Place, Leek, Staffordshire ST13 5HH (telephone: 0538 381000). Contact: David A. Hallen, 10 Derby Street, Leek, Staffordshire ST13 5AW (telephone: 0538 399332).

Cheddleton Flint Mill, Cheddleton.
3 miles south of Leek on A520.

The mill is in the Cheddleton valley on the west side of the road and is run by the Cheddleton Flint Mill Industrial Heritage Trust. This mill prepared raw materials for the pottery industry and is an important industrial monument. There are two external waterwheels turned by the river Churnet. The Caldon Canal runs next to the mill and the Trust's narrow boat *Vienna* is permanently moored at the wharf. Open throughout the year, daily 10-5. Contact: E. E. Royle, 5 Caroline Crescent, Brown Edge, Stoke-on-Trent, Staffordshire ST6 8SL (telephone: 0782 502907).

The Cornmill, Cornmill Lane, Tutbury.
On the Rolleston road, off A50 (Burton-upon-Trent to Stoke-on-Trent road), half a mile from the village centre and 3 miles from A38.

This early eighteenth-century corn mill produced flour until 1908 and subsequently became part of a tannery in 1914. There are two low-breast undershot wheels 12 feet in diameter with cast-iron

Cheddleton Flint Mill, Staffordshire, prepared raw materials for the pottery industry.

axles and rims and wooden spokes and paddles. The building has been renovated on three storeys and now contains a shop and tearoom next to the adjacent tannery. Open: all year except for Bank Holidays, Tuesday to Saturday 9-5.30. Party visits March to October. Details from Chapman Sheepskin Ltd, The Cornmill, Tutbury, Staffordshire DE13 9HA (telephone: 0283 813300).

The Mill, Mill Street, Stone.

This mill (c.1795) ceased work in the early 1970s and is now used as a licensed restaurant. The surviving mill features include the waterfall that cascades into the original wheelpit and an impressive 13 foot spur wheel. In the nearby old mill house (now a hotel), Richard 'Stoney' Smith was born. He gave the world Smith's Patent Germ Flour (1887), which later became Hovis. This well-known trade name was coined by an Oxford schoolmaster, Herbert Grime, who contracted the Latin couplet *hominis vis* (the strength of man). Open daily during normal licensing hours. Group visits contact: Mr B.V. Ayres, The Mill Hotel and Restaurant, Mill Street, Stone, Staffordshire ST15 8BA (telephone: 0785 818456).

Shugborough Park Farm, Milford.

The mill has been restored to working order and operates on most Sundays. There is a low-breast wheel, 19 feet 8 inches in diameter by 5 feet wide, which works two pairs of stones, a hoist and a collection of barn machinery via a lineshaft. The tailrace is enclosed in a brick culvert. An earlier, sixteenth-century mill on this site was used for fulling cloth. A century or so later it became a paper mill and in the Victorian era it became a corn mill. The mill was restored in 1988. This mill forms part of a working farm museum. Café. Open: Easter to October, daily 11-5; party bookings at any time. Contact: G. Marsden, Shugborough Park Farm, Milford, Stafford ST17 0XA (telephone: 0889 881388).

Town Mill, Stafford.

There has probably been a watermill on this site by the river Sow in Mill Bank since 1086. The last mill was demolished in 1957 but the wheels have been preserved *in situ*.

SUFFOLK

Flatford Mill, East Bergholt.

This former corn mill on the north bank of the Stour belonged to John Constable's father and the artist worked here for about a year. The surrounding country provided Constable with inspiration for his pictures. None of the machinery remains and there is no wheel. Since 1943 the mill and Willy Lott's Cottage have been owned by

The Mill in Stone, Staffordshire, is now a restaurant but the mill house was the birthplace of the miller who devised Hovis.

Alton Mill was dismantled and reconstructed here at the Museum of East Anglian Life in Stowmarket.

the National Trust. The property is leased by the Field Studies Council but the buildings and grounds are not open to public view.

Letheringham Watermill

This picturesque eighteenth-century mill near Easton was in working order until the 1940s, when the machinery was removed to Kelsale windmill. The mill building and 14 foot wood and cast-iron wheel have been beautifully restored. This mill is well known for its splendid gardens, water-meadows and woodland walk by the river Deben. Well appointed tearoom. Open for charity most Sundays in April, May, July and August, 2-6. See local press for details. Group bookings by arrangement. Contact: Rod Allen, Letheringham Mill, Woodbridge, Suffolk IP13 7RE (telephone: 0728 746349).

The Mill Hotel, Walnut Tree Lane, Sudbury.

The 16 foot undershot cast-iron wheel of this mill with its forty paddles can still be seen turning in the hotel's Meadow Bar behind plate-glass screens. In its working days the 8 foot wide wheel powered four sets of millstones and other ancillary machinery. The maker's name, Whatmore & Benyon of Wickham Market, and the date 1889 are still visible on the spokes. Contact: Mr D. Lord (telephone: 0787 75544).

Museum of East Anglian Life (Alton Mill), Stowmarket.

This interesting mill was removed to the museum from Stutton when Alton Water reservoir was under construction. It has all the machinery, which includes three pairs of stones and an overshot wheel. The mill, cart lodge and miller's house preserve their original grouping. The large Boby Building, a nineteenth-century woodworking and machinery erecting shop, contains major exhibitions on East Anglia's industrial heritage. Shop. Open: March to October, daily, 10-5. Evening and party visits by arrangement. Education centre available to schools. Contact: the Curator, Museum of East Anglian Life, Stowmarket IP14 1DL (telephone: 0449 612229).

Pakenham Mill, Grimstone End, near Ixworth.

Half a mile south of Ixworth, between A143 and A1088. Signposts from the Ixworth bypass (A143) and from the centre of Pakenham.

The parish of Pakenham is unique in Britain as it possesses both a working watermill and a working windmill. The watermill site was used in 1086. Recent excavations revealed the remains of a Tudor mill which preceded the existing eighteenth-century building. Pakenham Mill is a very fine pantiled building of five bays with three floors above the ground. The millpond was formed by building a dam across a tributary of the Blackbourn. This work created a fall of 10 feet to drive the wheel. The existing two o'clock

Pakenham Mill, Suffolk, is a fine pantiled building dating from the eighteenth century.

The tide mill at Woodbridge in Suffolk.

wheel was built by Peck of Bury St Edmunds and installed *c.*1900. There are three pairs of under-driven stones. Shop, picnic area. Open: Easter weekend to September, Wednesdays, weekends and Bank Holidays 2-5.30. Groups by arrangement throughout the year. Contact: Honorary Curator, R. Gillingham, 9 Mouse Lane, Rougham, Bury St Edmunds, Suffolk IP30 9JB (telephone: 0359 70570 or 0787 247179). (Visitors are also recommended to visit Pakenham windmill: see *Discovering Windmills*.)

Woodbridge Tide Mill
The machinery in this eighteenth-century tide mill has been completely restored. There are photographs and displays to inter-

est both students and visitors. The machinery operates at specific times subject to tides. See details at the mill or tourist information centres. The mill is situated on a busy quayside and looks over the yacht harbour (river Deben) and towards the site of the Sutton Hoo Ship Burial. There are several car parks in the vicinity. Group bookings in daylight hours. Open: Easter, and May to September, daily 11-5; October, Saturdays and Sundays 11-5. Contact: Geoff Gostling (Warden), 5 Carol Avenue, Martlesham, Woodbridge, Suffolk IP12 4SR (telephone: 0473 626618).

SURREY

Cobham
A quarter of a mile from Cobham village on the A245 Leatherhead road.

This small mill on the river Mole has a low-breast wheel 14 feet 6 inches in diameter by 3 feet 6 inches wide, which drives one pair of stones and the sack hoist. Although mills have probably occupied this site since 1086, the present structure dates from 1822. For opening times contact: Pamela Dick, Honorary Secretary, Cobham Mill Preservation Trust, 18 Church Street, Cobham, Surrey KT11 3EG (telephone: 0932 864393).

Coltsford Mill, Hurst Green.
The mill, still possessing its original machinery in working order, has been converted into a restaurant. The machinery can be seen in motion behind a glass partition. Open: Wednesday to Saturday, dinner from 7; Sunday, lunch only, 12-4. Contact: Lesley Moore, Coltsford Mill, Mill Lane, Hurst Green, Oxted, Surrey RH8 9DG (telephone: 0883 713962).

Haxted Mill and Museum, near Edenbridge.
Beside the road which joins B2029 at Lingfield Common with B2026 at Edenbridge.

Fully functional, this mill on the river Eden has a collection of milling bygones from many places and working waterwheels. Open: April to September, Wednesday, Saturday, Sunday and Bank Holidays 1-5. Group bookings at other times by arrangement. Contact: Howard Furness, Haxted Watermill and Museum, Haxted Road, Haxted, Edenbridge, Kent (telephone: 0732 865720).

Painshill Park, Portsmouth Road, Cobham.
This picturesque landscape, created between 1738 and 1773, is now in the care of the Painshill Park Trust. The spectacular 30 foot diameter undershot wheel was designed to pump water from the river Mole to the man-made lake. It was made by Joseph Bramah &

Haxted Mill has two working waterwheels and a milling museum.

Son *c.*1834 and replaced an earlier wheel. This second wheel worked until *c.*1960 and was restored in 1987 by Dorothea Restorations (Bristol). There is also a horse-operated pump dating from the Victorian period. Open: April to October, Sundays 11-5. School and party visits by arrangement with the Painshill Park Education Trust, Portsmouth Road, Cobham, Surrey KT11 1JE (telephone: 0932 866743).

Shalford Mill
South of Guildford on A281, opposite the Sea Horse inn.
This National Trust mill, dating from the eighteenth century, has a wheel and some machinery. A descriptive leaflet is available. Open at reasonable times by request. Apply to the Custodian, Shalford Mill, The Street, Shalford, Surrey GU4 8BS (telephone: 0483 61617).

WARWICKSHIRE

Arrow Mill, Alcester.
Now a restaurant on the river Arrow, the mill ceased working in the 1960s. The wheel still turns and can be viewed from the restaurant and lounge. Telephone: 0789 762419.

Charlecote Mill, Hampton Lucy.
The structure of this working mill probably dates from the

John Bedington, the miller, at Charlecote Mill, Hampton Lucy.

eighteenth century. In Domesday times the mill here was valued at six shillings and eight pence. There are two 18 foot diameter wheels. William Witherington, a former miller, who worked here from 1845 to 1864, carved his name in the brickwork on the top floor. Since 1978 the mill has been leased by John Bedington. In that year the west wheel was repaired at the expense of the BBC for the film *The Mill on the Floss.* Guide leaflet. Open to visitors on most Bank Holidays or by appointment. Contact: John Bedington, Charlecote Mill, Hampton Lucy, Warwickshire CV35 8BB (telephone: 0709 842072).

Wellesbourne Watermill
Just outside the village off B4086 to Kineton.

This is a working mill. There are a picnic water-meadow, wild-life and farm animals. It is a good location for a family visit. The tearooms serve scones baked with the mill's flour. Party visits by arrangement. Open: October to Easter, Sunday 1-4.30; Easter to September, Thursday to Sunday 10.30-4.30; Bank Holidays 11-4.30. Contact: Wellesbourne Watermill, Mill Farm, Kineton Road, Wellesbourne, Warwickshire CV35 9HG (telephone: 0789 470237).

WEST MIDLANDS

Sarehole Mill, Cole Bank Road, Birmingham.
In the suburb of Hall Green at the junction of Wake Green Road and Cole Bank Road.

The mill is part of the City of Birmingham Museum. The first mill here was probably built in the sixteenth century. Matthew Boulton was the tenant at Sarehole from 1756 to 1761. The existing fabric was rebuilt shortly after his tenancy. By the end of the eighteenth century the mill was equipped to grind edged tools and for a time it served a dual purpose. There are two waterwheels. The two o'clock wheel is on the north side, but the south wheel is overshot. Each wheel has its own train of gears and these can be seen from the ground floor. There are displays illustrating aspects of milling, blade grinding and English rural pursuits. Nearby is the house in which J. R. R. Tolkien lived between 1896 and 1900. He remembered Sarehole Mill when he wrote *The Lord of the Rings*. Two leaflets, 'The Tolkien Discovery Trail' and 'Tolkien and Sarehole Mill', are available from the mill. Open: April to October, daily 2-5. Times are subject to alteration; please contact Birmingham Museums and Art Gallery, Chamberlain Street, Birmingham B3 3DH (telephone: 021-235 2834).

WEST SUSSEX

Burton Mill
On a minor road off A285 south of Petworth and Coultershaw Bridge. A signpost indicates the turning.

Situated below a former seventeenth-century hammer pond, the mill (1784) was worked until *c.*1900. There were then two waterwheels driving four pairs of stones. These were replaced by turbines to generate electricity for Burton Park. Restoration work began in 1978 and one pair of flour stones is now operated by a water turbine. Wheatmeal and wholemeal flour, cereals and bran are produced. There is a nature trail of about 2 miles around the

Sarehole Mill is part of the Birmingham Museum service. It has two waterwheels. The mill has associations with the author J. R. R. Tolkien, who lived nearby early in his life.

millpond. Open: all year, Sunday 10.30-1; April to October, also Monday, Tuesday, Wednesday and Saturday 2-4. Arrangements for parties: Burton Mill Cottage, Petworth, West Sussex (telephone: 07987 293).

Coultershaw Pumphouse

About 1 1/2 miles south of Petworth on the river Rother where it is crossed by the A285 Petworth to Chichester road.

This smaller version of the Claverton Pump, Avon, has been painstakingly restored by members of the Sussex Industrial Archaeology Society. It was constructed in 1784 to pump water to Petworth and is a three-throw beam pump with a breastshot 1 foot wheel. As the wheel rotates it operates timber beams that are connected to the pump's three cylinders. Open: April to September, on the first and third Sunday in each month, 11-4. Party visits can be arranged at other times: R. M. Palmer, 11 Arlington Close, Goring-by-Sea, Worthing, West Sussex BN12 4ST (telephone: 0903 505626).

Ifield Mill

Approached from the Ifield to Rusper road via Hyde Drive and then a bridleway: grid reference TQ 246365 (OS Landranger sheet 187).

The four-storey building with its brick lower base and boarded upper floors can be seen from the roadway. It stands by a large millpond which was constructed in the sixteenth century to provide power for an ironworks. Corn milling began on the site in the seventeenth century. This mill worked until 1927. Restoration began in 1974. The fabric has been repaired and the overshot wheel, 12 feet in diameter and 12 feet wide, has been renewed. The launder has been restored using materials from Hammond's Mill at Burgess Hill. Voluntary workers are now engaged on the restoration of the gears. The object is to restore one pair of stones to working order. There is a small exhibition area on two of the mill floors. Parties and individuals are admitted by appointment. Open: all year, Sundays and Wednesdays 2-4. Contact: Honorary Secretary (telephone: 0293 523481).

Weald and Downland Open Air Museum, Singleton.

On A286 (Chichester to Midhurst road) about 7 miles north of Chichester. The museum is on the eastern side of the village and clearly signposted.

The reconstructed Lurgashall Mill is now set in the splendid surroundings of the Weald and Downland Open Air Museum among many other important buildings gathered together from the southern counties. The mill's cast-iron overshot wheel was origi-

nally made for Coster's Mill, West Lavington. Lurgashall Mill is
in regular operation during the summer season. It is used for
grinding corn for flour and animal feed. The wheel works two pairs
of stones, a grain cleaner and a sack hoist. The oldest parts of the
building may date from the seventeenth century. Many changes
were made to the building and machinery during its working life,
which lasted until the 1930s. Stoneground flour is on sale. Open:
March to October, daily 11-6 (last admissions 5); November to
February, Wednesday and Sunday only (daily from 26th December to 1st January) 11-5. Parties and school visits by appointment.
Contact: Weald and Downland Open Air Museum, Singleton,
Chichester, West Sussex PO18 0EU (telephone: 024363 348).

Wood's Mill, Henfield.

*One mile south of Henfield on the east side of A2037, at the
junction with Horn Lane.*

The mill was refurbished in the 1850s. Caleb Coote was the last
miller until 1927. The original machinery has been replaced but the
visitor can still see how a mill operated and watch the waterwheel
turning. Owned by the Sussex Wildlife Trust, the building now
houses a wildlife and countryside exhibition. Open: Good Friday
to last weekend in September, Tuesdays, Wednesdays and Thursdays in school holidays only and all Saturdays 2-6; Sundays and

*Lurgashall Mill has been reconstructed at the Weald and Downland Open
Air Museum, Singleton, West Sussex.*

Armley Mills in Leeds was built for fulling cloth, and now houses the Leeds Industrial Museum.

Bank Holidays 11-6. Group bookings by arrangement. Light refreshments available. Contact: Mike Russell, Manager, Wood's Mill Countryside Centre, Henfield, West Sussex BN5 9SD (telephone: 0273 492630).

WEST YORKSHIRE

Armley Mills, Leeds.

The magnificent Georgian mill is itself an important industrial monument. Its cylindrical cast-iron columns and T-section beams supporting the brick-arched floors were designed to resist the ravages of fire and it is the oldest surviving structure of its type. Armley Mills made good use of the abundant waters of the river Aire. A former fulling mill was driven by two gigantic wheels here, 18 feet in diameter and 28 feet wide, called Wellington and Blucher, each generating about 70 horsepower. Although they were removed in 1888 their wheelpits can still be seen. Visitors can see the working waterwheel, the fulling stocks, the textile gallery, steam engines and an engineering exhibition. Shop. Cinema. Parties by arrangement. Open: all year, Tuesday to Saturday 10-4, Sunday 2-4; closed Mondays (except Bank Holidays). Contact: the Curator, Leeds Industrial Museum, Armley Mills, Canal Road, Leeds, West Yorkshire LS12 2QF (telephone: 0532 637861).

Bradford Industrial Museum

Housed in a former mill, the museum preserves the industrial heritage of the city and district. Displays feature engineering and textiles. There are examples of prime movers which powered local manufacturing industries, and textile machinery illustrating the process of worsted cloth manufacture is demonstrated daily. The 10 foot diameter overshot waterwheel originally powered a sawmill in Nidderdale from 1860 to 1910. In 1923 it was moved to another sawmill and continued to be used until 1947. The wheel is demonstrated several times daily using electrical power for technical reasons. All parts of this remarkable site are accessible to disabled visitors. Open: Tuesday to Sunday 10-5; closed Mondays (except Bank Holidays), Christmas Day, Boxing Day and Good Friday. Contact: Mr S. Kerry, Bradford Industrial Museum, Moorside Road, Eccleshill, Bradford, West Yorkshire BD2 3HP (telephone: 0274 631756).

Thwaite Mills, Thwaite Lane, Leeds.

Between the river Aire and the Aire & Calder Canal, and about 2 miles south of Leeds city centre.

Before the present mill was built (1823-5) a fulling mill occupied the site. There are two low breastshot wheels with iron rims and wooden buckets. Both wheels have a diameter of 18 feet; one is 14 feet 6 inches wide and the smaller one 8 feet 9 inches. At twelve revolutions per minute the large wheel generates about 34 horsepower. Seed crushing and oil refining were the main trades in the 1830s. In 1872 the mill changed hands and flint or china stone grinding and whiting were the principal products. The flint or china stone was used in making glazes for the pottery industry. Chalk formed the basis of the whiting, putty or polish produced. The machinery used in these processes remains to fascinate the visitor; edge runner stones, a flint-grinding tub, putty mills and bucket pumps can all be seen. An excellent leaflet explains the function of this unique and important mill's component parts. The former manager's house is now used for displays and exhibitions. Dudley Row Cottages, demolished in 1968, where the workers once lived, will eventually be rebuilt. Access to all areas for disabled visitors. Open: all year, Tuesday to Sunday 10-5; closed Mondays except Bank Holidays. Contact: the Curator, Thwaite Mills, Stourton, Leeds LS10 1RP (telephone: 0532 496453).

WATERMILLS IN NORTHERN IRELAND

Annalong Cornmill, County Down.
At Annalong Harbour, 6 miles south of Newcastle on the Mourne coast.

Built about 1800, the mill houses a grain-drying kiln, three sets of stones and ancillary machinery. It is powered by a 15 foot diameter wheel and a 1920s Marshall 'hot bulb' paraffin engine. Owned by Newry and Mourne District Council, it has been restored to full working order, producing flour and oatmeal. There are guided tours and a milling exhibition. Open: Easter to June, Saturday and Sunday 2-6; July and August, Friday and Saturday 2-6; September and October, Saturday and Sunday 2-6. Group bookings March to November. Contact: Tourist Department, Newry and Mourne District Council, Greenbank, Newry, County Down BT34 8UA (telephone: 0693 67226); or Annalong Cornmill (telephone: 03907 68736).

Castle Ward Sawmill, County Down.
In the grounds of the well-known National Trust house, west of Strangford village on A25. Entrance by Ballyculter Lodge, 7 miles north-east of Downpatrick.

This water-powered sawmill is now a rarity in the British Isles. This restored example is part of the lower farmyard complex which was the focus of the estate's working life and is an interesting technical survival. The Castle Ward corn mill is being restored and will eventually be opened to the public. It has a 13 foot by 5 foot wheel. Visitors to Castle Ward will also want to see the house and grounds. Tearooms. The sawmill is open every day from dawn to dusk. Working demonstrations depend upon an adequate water supply. Party visits and demonstrations can be arranged. Telephone: 039686 204.

Ulster Folk and Transport Museum, Cultra, Holywood, County Down.
Just outside Belfast, at Cultra, Holywood.

Coalisland Water-powered Spade Mill was built in 1840 and worked until 1950. It was reconstructed at the museum in 1964, after it had ceased to work. It has breastshot waterwheels, the larger to power a great hammer which beat out the blades and the smaller to drive a powerful fan to provide draughts to the fires. The rough spade was forged in the mill using the massive trip hammer. It was finished in the adjoining building, which now houses an

The Coalisland Spade Mill at Ulster Folk and Transport Museum.

exhibition illustrating the processes involved in spade manufacture. Spades had an important role in Irish agriculture.

At Gorticashel Water-powered Flax Scutching Mill, the breastshot waterwheel drove cogged rollers to break up the flax and rotating blades to separate the fibres from the stalk case. The mill was erected in the Sperrin Mountains in the 1850s and worked until about 1950. Scutching was the process of separating the outer casing and inner core of the flax from the fibres used to spin linen thread.

The museum gives an authentic glimpse into what life was like at the turn of the century. The outdoor museum has been created through bringing original buildings from all over Ulster and reconstructing them within the museum's extensive 176 acre site overlooking Belfast Lough. Parties by arrangement. Special provision has been made for visitors with mobility difficulties. Open: October to March, Monday to Friday 9.30-4, Saturday and Sunday 12.30-4.30; April, May, June, September, Monday to Friday 9.30-5, Saturday 10.30-6, Sunday 12-6; July and August, Monday to Saturday 10.30-6, Sunday 12-6. Contact: Ulster Folk and Transport Museum, Cultra, Holywood, Belfast BT18 0EU (telephone: 0232 428428; fax: 0232 428728).

Wellbrook Beetling Mill, County Tyrone.
About 4 miles west of Cookstown.

Beetling is the finishing process in linen manufacture which gives the cloth a smooth glossy surface by the action of wooden

Wellbrook Beetling Mill was used in the finishing of linen cloth.

hammers. In a beetling mill the hammers are raised by a wiper beam powered by the waterwheel. The wiper beams in this mill (*c.*1830) are nearly 12 feet long and have a diameter of 15 inches. Each beam lifts 32 beetles (hammers). There are seven beetling engines. The external breastshot wheel is 16 feet in diameter and 4 feet 6 inches wide. It is a hybrid wheel with an iron centre and rim but wooden spokes and buckets. After the cloth had been through the machines it was taken to the drying loft on the first floor, which has louvred windows to regulate the draught. Mill shop. Open: April, May, June and September, Saturdays, Sundays and Bank Holidays 2-6; Easter, daily 2-6; July, August, daily except Tuesday 2-6. Contact: 06487 51715 or 51735.

WATERMILLS IN SCOTLAND

GRAMPIAN

Old Mills, Elgin.
On the river Lossie, a quarter of a mile north of A96 in Elgin.
This working meal mill has two low-breast wheels. It is a substantial stone structure with an interesting exterior. Open: April to September, daily except Mondays 9-5. Group bookings by arrangement, including out-of-season visits. Exhibition and interpretative centre. Working model mill. Coffee bar. Contact: Mike Dinwoodie (miller), Old Mills Visitor Centre, Old Mills Road, Elgin, Moray IV30 1YH (telephone: 0343 540698).

HIGHLAND

Glendale Watermill, Duirinish, Isle of Skye.
On the west coast of Loch Pooltiel.
This is a small thatched stone mill which has a metal overshot wheel installed in 1902. The mill last worked commercially in 1914 and was restored to working order in 1972. On most days

Preston Mill in Lothian has a circular drying kiln with a conical roof.

when the mill is open the wheel is operated. Open: April to September, daily 10-6; November to March, by appointment only. Enquiries to: Mr W. MacKenzie, 18 Holmisdale, Glendale, Isle of Skye (telephone: 047081 316).

Highland Folk Museum, Duke Street, Kingussie.

This regional museum contains displays illustrating many aspects of the Highland way of life. The Norse mill from Back, Isle of Lewis, with its horizontal wheel was brought here in the 1940s. Until the 1900s it was operated and owned collectively by five crofters. It is called a clack mill, a name derived from the noise made by the feed shoe as it was shaken to make the grain fall into the eye of the stone. The mill is being refurbished and replacement machinery has been installed. When a water supply has been provided the mill will be shown working. Intending visitors should check progress with the museum. Open: November to March, Monday to Friday 10-3; April to October, Monday to Saturday 1-6 and Sunday 2-6. Party visits by arrangement: the Curator, Highland Folk Museum, Duke Street, Kingussie, Inverness-shire PH21 IJP (telephone: 0540 661307).

LOTHIAN

Preston Mill, East Linton.

Preston Mill is now owned by the National Trust for Scotland and it was restored to its present working state with the help of Rank Hovis McDougall plc. It is in a beautiful setting on the banks of the Tyne and among its features are the cast-iron wheel, made by Mathers of Fountainbridge, Edinburgh, at the beginning of the twentieth century, and the circular drying kiln with its conical roof. Andrew Meikle, the engineer, millwright and inventor, lived nearby and from his notebooks we know that he worked on this mill in 1749. Open: April to September, Monday to Saturday 11-1 and 2-5; October, Saturday 11-1 and 2-4, Sunday 2-4; last tour 20 minutes before closing, morning and afternoon. Contact: Mrs Frances Scott, Roselea Cottage, East Linton, East Lothian EH40 3DS (telephone: 0620 860426).

ORKNEY

Click Mill, Dounby.

This is a Norse type of horizontal mill and is unusual in having two sets of paddles on its upright shaft. The monument is open to the public at all reasonable times. Contact: Tourist Information Centre, Broad Street, Kirkwall, Orkney KW15 1NX (telephone: 0856 2856).

At Blair Atholl the mill has two pairs of stones used for milling oats.

TAYSIDE

Aberfeldy Watermill
Mill Street, Aberfeldy.

The mill was built in 1825 and takes its water from the Birks of Aberfeldy. There is a 15 foot diameter overshot wheel which powers two pairs of 54 inch diameter French burr stones, which each weigh 1½ tons. Visitors can see stoneground oatmeal being processed. The restoration was carried out by Tom Rodger, a miller from Cupar, in 1987 and the mill was awarded a Civic Trust Commendation for this work in 1988. Group bookings by arrangement including evenings. Open: Easter to October, Monday to Thursday 10-5; Sundays 12-5. Contact: Mill Manager, Aberfeldy Watermill, Mill Street, Aberfeldy, Perthshire PH15 2BG (telephone: 0887 20803).

Barry Mill, Carnoustie.

This eighteenth-century mill was opened at Easter 1992 after a three-year period of restoration. The mill was worked until 1980, when floods damaged its source of water. Barry Mill processed the oats from many of the local farms. It now works for demonstration purposes. Open: Easter and May to mid October, daily 11-1 and 2-5. Group visits by arrangement. Contact: Peter Ellis, Barry Mill, Barry, Angus DD7 7RH (telephone: 0241 53311).

Blair Atholl Mill

This mill ceased work in 1929, and it was used for storage for many years until a full restoration began in 1976. There is an external breastshot wheel, 16 feet in diameter and 4 feet 6 inches wide. Three grades of oatmeal and other milled products are produced on the two pairs of burr stones. Mill and tearoom open: April (or Easter if earlier) to October, weekdays 10-5, Sunday 12-5. Open Thursdays during the winter for sales only. Party visits by arrangement: John Ridley, Projects Ltd, The Mill, Blair Atholl, Pitlochry, Perthshire PH18 5SH (telephone: 0796 481321).

Lower City Mills, West Mill Street, Perth.

This fine mill is part of Britain's most complete group of Georgian mill buildings. Its internal wheel derives power from the 4 mile long millstream. The machinery in use dates from the nineteenth century. The oatmeal produced here provided porridge for most of the nation's prisoners. There is a mill shop, and the Kilnhouse Tea Room was once an oat-drying kiln. Educational visits can be arranged to suit a school's specific requirements. The quality of the restoration work carried out was recognised by a Times/RICS award in 1989 and a Civic Trust Award in 1990. Open: Easter to October, Monday to Saturday 10-5; Easter Sunday and Sundays in July and September 12-5; November to March, Tuesday to Saturday 10-4. Contact: Norman Smith, Lower City Mills, West Mill Street, Perth PH1 5PQ (telephone: 0738 30572).

WESTERN ISLES

Isle of Lewis

Two Norse horizontal mills have been preserved on the west coast of the island: at *Bragar*, a restoration by the West Side Historical Survey, 1981, and at *Shawbost*, a mill restored by the pupils of Shawbost School in 1970.

WATERMILLS IN WALES

Aberdulais Falls, Aberdulais, Neath.
The spectacular waterfall where the river Dulais drops 34 feet at Aberdulais has been exploited by industry since at least the sixteenth century — at first for copper smelting, then ironworking, corn milling and tinplate manufacture — and since the eighteenth century the dramatic scenery has drawn artists, including Turner, and tourists. Although the remains of earlier generations of water power are not easily traced, the National Trust, which now owns the site, has installed a 28 foot diameter waterwheel in the masonry pit of an earlier wheel and this drives a 200 kilowatt water turbine generating electricity that is fed into the National Grid. There is a visitor centre housing displays on the history of the site. Open: November to March, daily 11-4; April to October, Monday to Friday 11-5, Saturdays, Sundays and Bank Holidays 11-6. Telephone: 0639 636674.

Bersham Ironworks, Wrexham.
John Wilkinson's ironworks were converted to milling in the nineteenth century. All the machinery remains. Contact: Bersham Industrial Centre, Bersham, Wrexham, Clwyd (telephone: 0978 261529).

King's Mill (see page 105) and Bersham are part of the Clywedeg Valley Trail, a 9 mile open-air park with seven key attractions. Contact: Wrexham Tourist Information Centre, The Guildhall, Wrexham, Clwyd LL11 1AY (telephone: 0978 292015).

Blackpool Mill and Caverns, Canaston.
Near the A40 between Haverfordwest and St Clears.
Standing on the bank of the Eastern Cleddau, this is a restored 1813 corn mill with working waterwheel. In the caves there are lifesize models of prehistoric Welsh wild animals, and there is an exhibition of Victorian model steam engines. Mill shop and café. Picnic area nearby. Open: Easter to October, daily 11-6. Contact: Mrs Jean Hance, Blackpool Mill, Narberth, Dyfed (telephone: 0437 541233).

Brynkir Woollen Mill, Golan.
3 miles from Porthmadog at the entrance to the Cwm Pennant valley. From Caernarfon take A487 to Porthmadog and turn left to Golan about 3 miles after Bryncir.
This is a woollen mill with a waterwheel that still turns although the looms are powered by electricity generated by the water turbine. The mill shop sells woollen goods made on the premises.

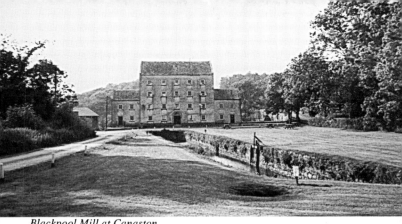
Blackpool Mill at Canaston.

Open: Monday to Thursday 8-4.45, Friday 8-4; closed Saturday, Sunday and Bank Holidays. Parties by arrangement: Brynkir Woollen Mill Ltd, Golan, Garndolbenmaen, Gwynedd LL51 9YU (telephone: 076675 236).

Carew Tidal Mill
Just off A4075 between Pembroke and Tenby.
This nineteenth-century tidal mill was in use until 1937. It has been renovated and is administered by the Pembrokeshire Coast National Park Authority. Open: Easter to October, daily 10-5. Parking at castle. Contact: G. M. Candler, Carew Castle, Carew, near Tenby SA70 8SL (telephone: 0646 651782).

Denant Mill, Haverfordwest.
In a rural setting off Dale Road (B4327), about 2 miles from Haverfordwest.
The stone mill house dates from the sixteenth century. Although the mill no longer works, the 12 foot diameter by 4 foot wide backshot wheel and its machinery are still *in situ* and accessible to visitors. Water from the original leat now flows, via the bypass sluice, into a new pond which provides a home for ducks. Restaurant. Open during business hours or by arrangement with the proprietor. Contact: Sydney Vincent, Denant Mill, Dreenhill, Haverfordwest, Dyfed SA62 3TS (telephone: 0437 766569).

Y Felin, St Dogmaels.
Follow the signpost to St Dogmaels from A487, then take the second left as you enter the village.
Y Felin is a water-powered mill producing a range of stoneground flours. The millpond adjacent to thirteenth-century St Dogmaels

Abbey provides water for the 14 foot overshot wheel. There are three pairs of stones. The mill is probably on the site of the earlier abbey mill, and some of the stonework may date from the fifteenth century. Open daily through the summer and on most days during the winter, 10.30-5.30. The tearoom is open daily (except Saturday) from Easter to October. For information telephone: 0239 613999.

Y Felin, Cenarth, Newcastle Emlyn.

There were mills at Cenarth on the river Teifi in the fourteenth century, but the present mill probably dates from the seventeenth century. It has an undershot wheel and this operates two pairs of stones. Wheat and oats are again ground at this mill, which worked until 1964. There is also an oat drier. The mill is part of the National Coracle Centre. Open: Easter to October, daily 10.30-5.30, and at other times by appointment. Contact: Martin Fowler, National Coracle Centre, Cenarth, Newcastle Emlyn, Dyfed SA38 9LJ (telephone: 0239 710980 or 710209).

Felin Crewi, Penegoes.

The mill was probably built in the mid sixteenth century. It worked until 1940, when the mill wheel was sold as scrap for ten shillings. The 15 foot 6 inch cast-iron undershot wheel now in use and the other machinery came from another local mill and were installed during restoration in 1985. This mill works throughout the year and its flour is used by bakeries over a wide area. Two of the mill floors have been partly cut away to allow for a new staircase and to enable visitors to see the machinery and the miller at work. This site with its additional wildlife attractions has been developed with disabled and wheelchair visitors in mind. Café and shop. It is a good location for children and school visits. Group visits by arrangement. Open: Easter to October, daily 10.30-5.30. Telephone for winter opening times. Contact: Patti Partridge, Felin Crewi Watermill, Penegoes, Machynlleth, Powys SY20 8NH (telephone: 0654 703113).

Felin Geri, Newcastle Emlyn.

At Cwm Cou, off B4333 from Newcastle Emlyn.

Felin Geri is a restored working mill supplying many local bakers with stoneground flour. It has two wheels in the same stream; both are overshot, but one is pitchback and powers the flour mills and the other is standard and drives a sawmill. Museum, bakery and shop. Open: Easter to October, Monday to Friday 10-6; Saturday and Sunday 10-4. Telephone: 0239 710810.

Felin Newydd, The Mill at Crugybar.

This is a typical Welsh upland mill with three floors. The 12 foot diameter by 3 foot wide wood and iron overshot wheel (fitted in 1907) is fed, via a duct three-quarters of a mile long, from the river Annell. There are two pairs of stones but only one is in use, and flour is usually ground on each of the eight daily conducted tours. Gold was mined a mile away and water from the same river was used for washing the ore. A fifteenth-century record shows that there was a mill here at that time, but the present structure probably dates partly from the seventeenth century. Graffiti inside, dated 1726, link the mill with Welsh colonists in Patagonia. Coaches by appointment. Group and school visits by arrangement. Open: Easter Saturday to 31st October, 10-6; closed Mondays (except Bank Holidays). First tour of mill 10.30; last tour 5.30. Contact: Malcolm Beeson, Felin Newydd, Crugybar, Llanwrda, Dyfed SA19 8UE (telephone: 05585 375).

King's Mill Visitor Centre, Wrexham.
In King's Mill Road, a mile south-east of the town. Signpost off A525 (the Wrexham to Whitchurch road).

This mill, part of the Erddig estate, was worked until 1940 and restored in 1989. There are a working overshot wheel and some machinery. The site possessed a mill in 1315. A new mill was built in 1769 and now visitors can meet John Lowe, the first miller in the new mill, who presents 'The Miller's Tale', an original interpretation of life and work here in the eighteenth century. There is an exhibition describing the mill's construction and the way it served the community. Shop. Group visits by arrangement. Open: Easter to September, Tuesday to Sunday and Bank Holidays 10-5. Contact: King's Mill Visitor Centre, King's Mill Road, Wrexham, Clwyd (telephone: 0978 362967 or 358916).

Llywernog Silver-Lead Mine, Ponterwyd.
Near A44 between Aberystwyth and Llangurig. The museum is on the coastal side of Ponterwyd village and can be clearly seen from the main road.

This old mine is being restored to show the miners' way of life and their working methods. Visitors can see a tape and slide presentation, a prospecting tunnel, an ore crusher, a miner's trail and the following waterwheels: 1, the mine's great wheel, 50 feet in diameter by 3 feet wide, under restoration (re-erection should be completed in 1994), and made at Hawarden Ironworks, Flint, *c*.1865; 2, a working 14 foot by 2 foot backshot wheel (*c*.1910) by Thomas Williams, Central Foundry, Aberystwyth; 3, a working 14 foot by 2 foot overshot wheel (*c*.1890) by Eagle Foundry, Aberystwyth; 4, a working 11 foot by 2 foot overshot wheel (*c*.1900) by Cardigan Foundry; 5, a working 8 foot 8 inch undershot 'dipper' wheel, newly made to demonstrate the principles of water raising;

6, a 4 foot 6 inch by 6 inch overshot farm pumping wheel by Irons of Wadebridge, Cornwall. Refreshments, shop and picnic area. Open: Easter to October, 10-4 (or dusk if earlier). Educational and group applications: Llywernog Silver-Lead Mine, Ponterwyd, Aberystwyth, Dyfed. Telephone: 097085 620 or 0545 570823 in winter.

Melin Maesdulais, Porthyrhyd.
8 miles south-east of Carmarthen.

This watermill began as a corn mill in the eighteenth century, became a woollen mill from about 1890 to 1925 and was converted back to become a commercial flour mill in 1977. It has a modern belt-drive system powered by a 15 foot overshot wheel. It is not now generally open to visitors, except group bookings, and schools are welcome. Licensed by the Soil Association for the manufacture of organic flours. Contact: Geoff or Phillipa Brace, Melin Maesdulais, Porthyrhyd, Carmarthen, Dyfed SA32 8BT (telephone: 0267 275472).

Melin Moelwyn, Tanygrisiau, Blaenau Ffestiniog.
Just outside Blaenau Ffestiniog and on the route of the Ffestiniog Railway.

Melin Moelwyn was a fulling mill established in its present form in the 1880s and which ran until 1964. It was restored with county council help in 1977-8. It is unusual because it is not in the traditional wool-processing area (around Dolgellau) and when it was built many fulling mills were already declining. This suggests that it may have replaced a previous fulling mill. Uniquely in this area, it retains its waterwheel and machinery. The fulling stocks are of the 'improved' Kilburn pattern with a cast-iron frame and were driven by an overshot waterwheel which also drove a milling machine, spinning machines and a nap-raiser. There is a museum. For information about the opening times contact: Area Archivist, Gwynedd County Council, Cae Penarlag, Dolgellau (telephone: 0341 422341).

Nant-y-Coy Mill, Treffgarne Gorge.
7 miles north of Haverfordwest on A40.

This old corn mill (*c.*1844) has a 13 foot 6 inch diameter overshot wheel with 39 buckets. There are three pairs of stones. A mill stood on this site in the fourteenth century. Visitors can also enjoy the nature walk, craft centre and museum. Open: Easter to early October, Tuesday to Saturday 10-5.30; July and August, Monday to Saturday 10-6, Sunday 2.30-5.30. Tearoom (available as a classroom out of season). Parties by arrangement. Contact: H. J. Wilson, Nant-y-Coy Mill, Treffgarne Gorge, Haverfordwest, Dyfed SA62 5LR (telephone: 043787 671).

Pentre Mill at Loggerheads Country Park in Mold.

National Centre for Alternative Technology, Llwyngwern Quarry, Machynlleth.
3 miles north of Machynlleth on the A487 Dolgellau road.

An internationally renowned display and education centre, promoting practical ideas and information on sustainable technologies and lifestyles, the Centre inspires and enables people to soften their impact on the natural world by demonstrating examples of wind and water power, appropriate technology, organic gardening and low energy dwellings. A unique water-powered railway ascends a 200 foot slope from the car park to the 7 acre display. There are a bookshop and restaurant on the site. Open to visitors 10-5 for most of the year; in winter it is advisable to check by telephone to find out if the CAT is temporarily closed for maintenance. Contact: Centre for Alternative Technology, Llwyngwern Quarry, Machynlleth, Powys SY20 9AZ (telephone: 0654 702400).

Pentre Mill, Loggerheads Country Park, Mold.
In Loggerheads Country Park on the A494 Mold to Ruthin road.

This corn mill probably dates from *c.*1796. In 1871 it was purchased by a timber merchant and it seems likely that the sawmill was added during the following decade. Before the mill ceased work in 1942 it had also been used to generate electricity and to churn butter. Open: June to September, Sunday afternoons, for self-guided mill visits. Group visits by appointment at any time. Visitor centre with information desk and shop, café and picnic areas. Car park at Country Park. Contact: Clwyd Countryside Service, Loggerheads Country Park, Mold, Clwyd CH7 5LH (telephone 0352 85614 or 85586).

Rock-Mill, Capel Dewi, Llandysul.
Follow Rock-Mill signs from Llandysul.

Rock-Mill is a small water-powered working woollen mill with an overshot wheel. The mill was built in 1890 by John Morgan, the great-grandfather of the present operator. This mill produces a wide selection of woollen goods, which can be purchased in the mill shop. All the production processes can be seen: carding, spinning and weaving. Picnic area. Open: all year, Monday to Friday 10-5; also Saturdays from Easter to September, 10-1. Contact: John Morgan & Son, Rock-Mill, Capel Dewi, Llandysul, Dyfed SA44 4PH (telephone: 0559 362356).

Swansea Maritime and Industrial Museum
Five minutes from city centre and the beach.

The machinery from the Abbey Woollen Mill, Neath, which was formerly water-powered, is on display. The daily operational processes which can be seen include carding, spinning and weaving. Blankets, shawls, rugs, etc, which are produced from 100 per cent Welsh wool can be purchased in the museum shop. Open daily, except Mondays, 10.30-5.30. Parking at adjacent leisure centre. Contact: D. Stephens, Maritime and Industrial Museum, Maritime Quarter, Swansea, SA1 1SN (telephone: 0792 650351).

Trefriw Woollen Mills, Trefriw.
In the centre of Trefriw on B5106.

This mill is powered by electricity derived from two Boving Pelton wheels. One turbine is used at a time. Visitors can see all the processes involved in the manufacture of bedspreads and tweeds. The mill started as an eighteenth- century 'Pandy' water-powered fulling mill and has belonged to the same family since 1859. The waterwheels were replaced by turbines in the early years of the twentieth century. Although the mill's present buildings are modern, many of the machines date from the 1940s. A large shop sells Welsh crafts, wool products and knitwear, and there is a café. Mill open: Easter to October, Monday to Friday 9-5.30. Weaving, turbine house, shop and café open all year, Monday to Friday 9-5.30. Contact: Elaine Williams, Trefriw Woollen Mills Ltd, Trefriw, Gwynedd LL27 0NQ (telephone: 0492 640462).

Welsh Folk Museum (Amgueddfa Werin Cymru), St Fagans, Cardiff.

The significant collection of buildings in this very fine museum includes four that are associated with water power.

Melin Bompren Corn Mill has been meticulously restored to the high standards set by Amgueddfa Werin Cymru. There is an external overshot waterwheel. The mill also has a corn-drying kiln which is an unusual feature. All the necessary machinery is on view.

Esgair Moel Woollen Mill is a complete woollen mill in working order. It formerly stood at Llanwrtyd in Powys, serving a local, predominantly rural market, and was not typical of the mills which performed specific processes. The mill building is 92 feet long and 18 feet 6 inches wide. It seems as if the waterwheel was at one time situated outside the building — on the gable. The strengthening of the structure enclosed the wheel, which is of particular interest as it has a wooden axle and clasp arms that are bolted to a cast rim. The paddles (spoons) are of elm and the wheel's diameter is 8 feet 4 inches. A tappet wheel which raises the hammers of the fulling mill is mounted on one side of the waterwheel and at the opposite side an iron cog (6 feet 8 inches in diameter) is attached. This cog drives the belt drum that operates the various machines. This mill is still a working mill and in it craftsmen produce cloth and blankets. The processes which may be observed by the visitor are dyeing, willying (teasing), carding, spinning, twisting, weaving, fulling and finishing.

Rhayader Tannery is a large range of stone and timber buildings which display all the stages of the conversion of hides to leather. An overshot waterwheel (now static) was used to grind bark for use in the tanning pits in which hides were immersed for as long as eighteen months.

Deheufryn Gorse Mill came from Colwyn, Clwyd. This small water-driven mill was used to crush and tear young gorse shoots for use as cattle fodder. The spiked rollers were driven directly from the axle of a wooden overshot wheel. The building, which dates from *c.*1850, has been rebuilt as a static exhibit.

Restaurants. Picnic areas. Bookshop. Open daily 10-5; closed Christmas Eve, Christmas Day, Boxing Day, New Year's Day. Discounts for party bookings. Contact: Marketing Department (National Museum of Wales), Welsh Folk Museum, St Fagans, Cardiff CF5 6XB (telephone: 0222 555105).

Welsh Slate Museum, Llanberis.

The museum is located within the former workshops of the Dinorwic slate quarry. The quarry closed in 1969 but its equipment and machinery have been preserved and visitors can see the foundry, the smithy, the steam locomotive and other rolling stock. The largest machine in the quarry is the waterwheel. A cog ring on its circumference transmitted power to a layshaft that operated the various machines. This vast wheel has a diameter of 50 feet 5 inches, is 5 feet wide and has 140 buckets. It was built by De Winton & Company of Caernarfon in 1870. The water to feed it came from the other side of the valley in 2 foot diameter cast pipes. Visitors can now see this immense pitchback wheel working. There are slate-splitting displays. An operating Pelton wheel can be seen in the museum. Open: Easter to September, 9.30-5.30. Parties, schools and out-of-season visits by arrangement. Contact: The Welsh Slate Museum, Gilfach Ddu, Llanberis, Gwynedd LL55 4TY (telephone: 0286 870630).

WATERMILLS IN THE CHANNEL ISLANDS

Le Moulin de Quetivel, St Peter's Valley, Jersey.
The mill building dates from the seventeenth century. This is Jersey's only mill in full working order and stoneground flour is still produced. There are an external 12 foot pitchback wheel and two pairs of stones. Since the 1940s the mill has been rebuilt and some machinery acquired from other local mills. In 1979 the mill received a Civic Trust Award for the quality of the restoration. There is a video presentation, an exhibition of milling, a kitchen display, mill shop, herb garden and woodland walk. The car park is next to the millpond, a short walk from the mill. Open: May to October, Tuesday, Wednesday and Thursday 10-4. Contact: the Secretary, National Trust for Jersey, The Elms, St Mary, Jersey JE3 3EN (telephone: 0534 483193).

FURTHER READING

Clark, C., *et al. The Great Laxey Wheel and Mine.* Institute of Industrial Archaeology, 1985.

Darrow, K., and Rick, P. *Appropriate Technology* (volume 1). Appropriate Technology Project, Stanford, California, 1976.

Long, G. *The Mills of Man.* Herbert Joseph, 1931.

Reynolds, John. *Windmills and Watermills.* Hugh Evelyn, 1970.

Syson, Leslie. *British Watermills.* Batsford, 1965.

Syson, Leslie. *The Watermills of Britain.* David & Charles,1980.

Taylor, R.H. *Alternative Energy Sources.* Adam Hilger, 1983.

Vince, John. *Discovering Windmills.* Shire, eighth edition, 1993.

Vince, John. *Power before Steam.* John Murray, 1985.

INDEX

Page numbers in italics refer to illustrations.